CONVERSATIONS
ON THE STYX

CONVERSATIONS ON THE STYX

by

MATTHIAS R. HEILIG

PHILOSOPHICAL LIBRARY

New York

"It is better to speak wisdom foolishly like the saints, than to speak folly wisely like the deans."

— Chesterton

"I never made a mistake in my life,—at least never one that I could not explain away afterwards."

— R. Kipling

"Wise men talk because they have something to say; fools, because they have to say something."

— Plato

CONTENTS

AS TO THESE CONVERSATIONS —

One of the motives which prompted these "Incidents" was the thought that we moderns are too greatly engrossed in the ethos of the present. Everything old is suspect. It must be deficient in some respect, we think; for, the wise ones of old were without adequate concepts of the relations of cause and effect. No one had discovered the true nature of matter; nor had Nature hinted any solution to the mystery of existence, or revealed the means by which Today has come out of the vast and shrouded Yesterdays!

No doubt we are the people! And those who lived long ago were painfully primitive, with neither ambition nor courage to explore the tremendous possibilities of Nature, and the uninhibited use of their wits. In fact, whenever any genius in ancient times displayed a wholly new idea, he was risking not only his reputation, but his very life.

The opinions we have of "old timers," however, are not always just. In many spheres of thought and action, the ancients reached an apex of inspiration, or a perception of basic truth, which ranks with the best of current efforts. The past was not "a bucket of ashes"!

Why cannot we short-lived individuals in this sensational era take time to review and think upon the evolving life of Mankind as our own preparation for a mature attitude toward Life? Surely, the total residuum of wisdom and truth, and the achievements of Man as a responsible agent of progress, are of greater significance than the values of today's gigantic material structures, colossal engines, and terrifying inventions for homicide!

Ancient thinkers had some great ideas. Of many a savant, saint and martyr of old, it can be said: "He being dead yet speaketh!"

BELLEROPHON SWATS THE GADFLY

It is probably true that mythology was a necessary first step in the conformation of mankind's philosophies, sciences and morals. Most myths seem absurd to us in the light of modern intelligence; but doubtless our seasoned and sapient systems will appear to be equally inadequate in A.D. 4066.

Of all the shadowy characters on the Styx, originating in those early misty epochs through which historic times fitfully filtered, Bellerophon was the most provocative.

I had been walking along the left bank of the Styx for several parasangs, among stately trees which reminded me of our willows, over acres of flowering moss and something which reminded me of our grass of Parnassus, when I reached a sudden rise of ground, on the rounded summit of which, on a marble bench, sat Bellerophon.

He was reading Hesiod. A copy of Homer's poems lay at his feet. I gazed at him awhile in silent admiration. As I approached him I heard him muttering; and soon I was near enough to hear him say:

"Preposterous assumption! unmitigated rot!"

"For what kind of wisdom are you looking in one so ancient?" I asked.

"I was curious to see," he replied, without looking up, "whether those who lived nearer the origin of things would know something about the manner and means by which the things that *are* came out of the things that *were.*"

"But," said I, "both Hesiod and the more ancient Homer lived too recently. Modern anthropologists are agreed that man lived fifty thousand years or more in a state of sub-ethical, half self-conscious stupidity before he had the wit to invent the charming

1

bedtime stories known as mythical lore. However, it seems to have been a success from the start. Its popularity was so great that in competition with it, serious drama, history, philosophy, and religion had to beg for a bare existence."

"You are forgetting," said he, "that much of mythology was the primordial effort to record history, the first feeble attempt to express philosophic ideas, and that it was the very matrix of religion — a necessary vehicle for its primitive expression."

"Oh," said I, "then you were not serious in condemning what you found in Hesiod."

"Wrong again," said he. "What I deprecate is the continuation and glorification of myth beyond its period of usefulness and out of its natural sphere. A seaweed is a very beautiful organism in its proper habitat, but a disgusting mass of slime when brought to land."

"Will not men always be 'children of larger growth', craving the graphic simplicity of. . . .?"

Bellerophon groaned. "You humans are always falling back upon your patterns of thought, your catch phrases, your categories, your clichés, your clever-sounding words. You observe how people act under certain stimuli and you catalogue the cause and effect. This you call knowledge. It is usually the most superficial observation of peripheral phenomena. You observe individuals of a class who are acting at variance with established norms, and you say the individuals have a 'fixation,' by which you mean 'an excessive concentration of the libido upon some idea or thing'."

"Well," I interrupted, "your ancient savants did not seem to arrive at any clearer understanding of the basic facts in man's psychic conditions, and of the laws governing the manifestations of the libido. . . ."

"That is the reason for their using myth," said he.

"To cover up their ignorance?"

"No; rather, to symbolize their inexpressible ideas," he continued. "The ancient teachers used such symbols as people could translate into proper feeling. But, of course, no symbol, no parable, no word, no painting, no song, no drama, no representation of any sort can, by even the utmost exercise of genius or knowledge, convey from one mind to another an exact definition or understanding of a given object, condition, or idea. In other words, reality is indescribable. And this is so because the mind has no

2

means of probing into its ultimate structure; nor has it vocabulary with which to express that which has never been, and can never be, experienced by the senses. In still other words: the more real, vital, and spiritual an idea is, the more inexpressible it becomes. And so it is that religious verities and moral imperatives must be conveyed to the feelings rather than to the intelligence."

"But," I objected, "is not the intelligence the final arbiter? Does it not decide what ideas shall be accepted and allowed to influence the emotions?"

"The intellect makes a brave showing; but the feelings decide the issue at last," said he, and then suddenly handing me the book, at which he had been glancing, exclaimed, "Look at this asinine illustration, designed to show me falling from Pegasus! I never fell from Pegasus! What is the idea back of this?"

"Is it possible," I replied, "that you do not know the rather well-established myth of the Gadfly? Zeus was said to have sent the gadfly to sting Pegasus, with the idea of unhorsing you before you succeeded in entering Elysium."

"That illustrates again the danger of extending the age of myth too far," mumbled Bellerophon, more to himself, I thought, than to me. "I have no doubt," he went on, "that early Greeks concluded that, as punishment for daring to wish to enter Elysium, Zeus actually sent that gadfly to sting the flank of good Pegasus. How right Hecataeus was that the legends of the Greeks are contradictory and ridiculous!"

"What," I asked hesitatingly, "is wrong with the legend?"

Bellerophon smiled. "Hardly," said he, "would Zeus have attempted to make a gadfly contradict its own nature. You see," he added, suddenly facing me, "the gadflies have instincts, and tropisms, and impulses, and stimuli — all worked out for them by nature and contingency through millennia of years. Zeus would not and could not influence the life and determine the particular action of a gadfly or of any other creature. As a matter of fact, no creature excepting man knows or can know what Zeus desires it to do. And man, even when he is reasonably sure of the divine will, can still refuse to obey it."

"The central idea," I said, "seemed to be that because of your presumption, Zeus wanted to keep you out of Elysium."

"The same error," he replied, "as is found in the Garden of Eden myth of the early Hebrews. Zeus welcomes all who wish

3

to come to Elysium, for no one really seeks the celestial abode unless he has a true spiritual sympathy with what is there. Thievish, lying, selfish, murderous, and sensual people know well enough that they *make* their place just what they themselves *are*. They know how bored, or ashamed, or uncomfortable, or frenzied they would become among the gods, heroes, and other great souls."

"I see," I answered weakly. There was a silence for awhile, and then I asked another foolish question.

"By the way, couldn't Zeus have made a strong wind blow that gadfly into the region where you were riding Pegasus?"

"How many times do you have to be told a thing?" said he. "Zeus is law-abiding. He would not interfere with the operations of nature, either in the inanimate, inorganic objects and forces or in living creatures, gadflies and others."

"But," I insisted, "you admitted that he would interfere with human conduct."

"When did I admit anything as absurd as that?"

"You said man is the only creature capable of knowing the divine will."

"So I did; and what do you infer from that?"

"Well," I replied, "what is it to reveal one's will to another, if it is not equivalent to trying to influence that other to obey?"

"Oh, this human ingenuity," he laughed, "which creates a complex system of logic to escape from the tyranny of ignorance, and straightway becomes the slaves of the system!"

"All right," said I, "explain it away; don't try to laugh it off. Explain how the Supreme *Nous* can have a will toward man and can design a nature which evidently reveals much of it, and yet not use his laws to persuade man to obey his will."

"The Supreme *Nous*," replied Bellerophon, "pays this high compliment to man, that he expects man to *try* to conduct himself as a *really independent* creature. To be sure, he *is* by nature, but *isn't* by the circumstance of his being a neurotic and hysterical victim of his imagination.

"You have been confusing the functions of similar categories of ideas — a very frequent error," Bellerophon continued, gradually becoming more earnest and emphatic. "You are assuming that the universe acts as you find mankind habitually disposed to act. It is a species of anthropomorphism. You see, for at least twenty thousand years self-conscious humans have been develop-

4

ing their now rather permanent and inherent spiritual characteristics: conscience, moral sensibilities, sense of fitness or the opposite, sense of integrity or its abuse, sense of abstract duty in relation to concrete action, and the versatile senses of honor, justice, love, beauty, relevancy, and progress. Well, as to emotional disposition and intellective equipment men are the natural products of the past.

"These mental powers are considered by men — and quite properly — to be spiritual and divine properties; that is, they are concerned with the nature of reality and the meaning and purpose of life. The employment of such powers — if the rules of reason and logic are valid — is the prerogative of responsible and creative spirits. Now, man is a creative, governing, progressive, meliorating creature. This manifest superiority over his environment dignifies man with a kind of reflected divinity.

"In using what is categorically just, ethical, true, beautiful, and creative of value, pleasure, and knowledge, man knows that he is exercising the natural *authority* of divinity; *and* he knows that the Supreme *Nous* wills the proper use of these virtues. This does not mean that man knows the will of the Supreme *Nous* completely or even extensively, but in sufficient degree. To the extent that man uses and experiments with these powers and elements in the laboratory of his thought, to that extent does he discover the will of the Supreme One. Or, put it in the passive voice, if you prefer: to that extent is the Supreme One revealed to man."

"And," I asked, "is the Supreme *Nous* not revealed in any other way?"

"In no other way," replied Bellerophon, and then added: "The soul becomes enlightened by experience — as man engages in constructive, creative, investigative work — by a certain cosmic spiritual upthrust; just as the trees of the forest develop fibrous and cellular stamina by a biologic upthrust or apogeotropism."

As I thought about it, that term seemed to me exceedingly significant.

"I believe," said I, "I could construct a whole theory of moral philosophy around that word 'apogeotropism.'"

Bellerophon grinned. "Still addicted to the human habits; still want to formulate systems around a symbol. Well, go ahead; how would you proceed?"

"Well," I began, "there are certainly contrary forces at work

5

everywhere and always. In general, the one is centrifugal, the other centripetal; one is gravitational, the other levitational; in some spheres one is anabolistic, the other katabolistic. Clearly in man we observe a force, or a whole category of forces, pulling him toward the earth, toward the lower planes of living — mentally, physically, socially, and in every material respect. *Facilis descensus;* and the majority let themselves gravitate.

"These forces which are geocentric are constant, ruthless, consistent, and law-abiding; in fact, they are necessary to the constitution of the present order. Yet man, to achieve his destined status, must resist them or establish a balance with them. They would spell ruin to man, should he surrender totally to them.

"Now, fortunately, another set of forces operates in man. These are the apogeotropic tendencies, which urge and energize man to lift himself and his condition up and above the low level of ignorance, vice, and all that is humanly inferior and degrading. These up-thrusting powers enable him to walk erect, literally and symbolically, and lend energy to those faculties by which he procures the higher values and produces the better elements of a superior life, ever improving conditions in himself and in his world, until finally he finds himself in Paradise itself."

"And," commented Bellerophon, "you are the one who approved of the myth in which Zeus was punishing me for trying to ride Pegasus into Elysium. Tch! tch! How consistent you mortals aren't!"

I had expected no encomiums from him, so I was not disappointed. I said, "I think I have been no more inconsistent than you. You repudiate the myth in one breath, and in the next ask me to interpret myth consistently."

"Why do we waste words on such silly ideas?" said he. "Tell me: do you consider that the myths of primitive people ought to provide the *permanent* bases of religious thought?"

"N-no; of course not," said I; "but I supposed that you . . . well . . . that you honored them sufficiently to sanction the system of metaphysical doctrines built upon the ideas underlying them."

"That has been done, alas, only too generally," said Bellerophon.

"Is it not true that myths arose out of misunderstanding of actual occurrences or from simple facts inadequately reported?" I asked.

"Many of them — my own included. You see," he went on, "Pegasus was a very remarkable horse — a 'sport,' your biologists

6

would have called him. He was eighteen hands high, very intelligent, and unbelievably speedy and enduring, yet most amiable and loyal. I was riding him around Mt. Olympus; and some pious citizens conceived the fancy that I was aspiring to scale the heights and enter the abode of the gods. They reported that we glided along without Pegasus' hoofs touching the ground."

"I envy you your experience with such an animal," I said.

"He was a remarkable creature," continued Bellerophon. "The truth about him would have been much more entertaining than the absurd legends invented about him."

"Yes," I replied, responding to his kindlier tone; "and yet, I recall how greatly as a boy I enjoyed the mysterious story of your wild flight into the celestial regions. I enjoyed the stories also of Hercules, and Cassiopeia, and Perseus. . . ."

"Such myths," said Bellerophon, "had at least one good result: they led early men to take an interest in astronomy. Everything men know of light and electric rays — electrons, protons, photons, and separated atoms — goes right back through the wild fancies of astrologers, on back to the stellified heroes whose immortal fame is recorded in the constellations." I assented; and he continued:

"And music, art, and literature, too, have been enriched by these childish fables. Milton's great epics, *Paradise Lost* and *Paradise Regained,* contain some of the noblest rhetoric in all literature. *Parsifal* is the greatest collection of sublime themes in a supported grandeur in the musical world. Myth was also a strong political factor. It had much to do with the unity of the early Egyptians and later Hebrews. Still later the Teutons, convinced that the Christian myth was a true revelation of man's miserable plight, and of his possible escape from the devil and his prison by the magic of sacred rites, plus a desperate faith and denial of their deep-seated passions, reluctantly gave up their brutal heroics, and indulged in battle only when they could deceive themselves into thinking they were practicing chivalry or protecting the interests of the church. Heinrich Heine spoke of this in his day. He credited Christianity with having calmed the brutal Nordic lust for battle, without eradicating the savage joy of conflict. The magic talisman, the cross, he said, was rapidly decaying. He prophesied what we have seen. 'The talisman,' he said, 'has been broken pathetically into pieces'; and the old stone gods rising from unremembered ruins, 'rubbing the

7

dust of a thousand years from their eyes,' have leaped to life to bring down their gigantic battle-axes on the Gothic cathedrals."

"In which case myths were not so wise and useful," I interrupted.

"Only because man tried to use them after their usefulness was spent."

"Should they have invented other myths?"

"No-o-o!" thundered Bellerophon; "the time for the serious contemplation of raw facts and undraped reality had come, but men loved the twilight of occultism more than the light. Traditions become very dear; and the birth of a new spirit is always painful and often dangerous."

"But," I began, thinking of the familiar and thrilling history of the Christian church, made precious by many a youthful association, and made impressive by heroism, authority, and weird prophecy — "but, hasn't the Christian myth proved to be the least offensive and the most successful religious system — the best possible religion for human kind?"

"No one can answer that," he replied; "simply because no one knows how another system might have worked. Perhaps a liberal mixture of Plato, Buddha, Moses, and Jesus, with proper eradication of tradition and myth and fiction, from time to time, as their superfluity was discovered, would have done much better than Athanasian and Anselmic Christianity."

"But, is it too late," I asked, "to get away from superfluous myths?"

"You propound somber riddles," said he. "My guess would be: it is too late. The world became too enthusiastic over mechanical toys, and came to find more joy in playing with scientific gadgets than in safeguarding its ethical and spiritual development. At length, the whole subject of character evolution became a matter of mechanistic adjustment of mind cells, which had inherited tendencies from both good and bad sources. Man, it was said, was inseparable from his past; and he behaved according to inherited patterns; and his most determined efforts to be free were but the inescapable illusions of a futile optimism."

"But," I interrupted, "this conception was repudiated by the savants of the early twentieth century."

"Yes, of course. Heisenberg taught that nature has no intention of being accurate, precise, and pattern-abiding in designing and evolving biological individuals and in planning their careers. The

8

indeterminism which he and his followers postulated gave much encouragement to those who still trusted in the freedom of the will, feeling it impossible to believe in an infallible causation, deeply concealed, like a stubborn Satan, in the nature of materiality."

"Which error, O Bellerophon, do you consider the worse," I asked humbly, "the pseudo-scientific or the pseudo-religious?"

"The latter," he replied without hesitation, "for a sane religious outlook would quiet all morbid fears and yet instil a respect for the moral imperatives. This respect for the categorical 'oughts' is better medicine than all your drugs and rest cures and diet regulations. But human beings will not think soberly about religion."

"You astonish me," I said, "when you intimate that people feel at all concerned about religion. I thought that the generations under fifty had given up their interest in the subject."

"You are not very observing," replied Bellerophon. "The people who *seem* to have forgotten religion have simply pushed the matter into their subconscious mind — where it creates twice as much disturbance as before. This accounts for suicides, nervous breakdowns, sadistic and other abnormal crimes, and the prevailing passion for gaiety and distracting entertainment among people who want to have no reverence for the ethical absolutes and stern realities of spiritual life."

"At the risk of stretching your patience beyond its limits," I said, "I would like to ask you to classify the pseudo-religious myths with reference to their importance as mischief makers."

He smiled, as if he suspected me of being sarcastic; but he complied after a short pause. "These are several categories of myths," he said. "The largest and nastiest group is that embracing the fancies which fan the flame of fear. Every religion has built upon the long-established dread of death. The temptation to utilize this as propagandism, abetted by bad conscience and anthropomorphic ideas of divine justice, was too great to resist. To the grim mystery of death was added the horror of hell. Dante gives us some notion of the grotesque villainies which the Deity was supposed to sanction or even devise as means of torturing ignorant sinners — which villainies were believed in with ghoulish relish by mediaeval saints.

"To the extent that the doctrine of hell has been discarded, the fear of the occult and of various substitutes for hell has come into vogue. Long ago it became such a habit to instil fear into youth — as a motive to modest and constrained conduct — that people

9

generally accepted the fear motive as quite proper and natural. Without being urged, they feared everything they did not understand. They feared the invisible, the inexplicable, the uncontrolled, the unpredictable, the powers of nature, the strength of aliens, the uncertainties of health and fortune, the unknown of tomorrow, and the mysteries of night.

"Life was just one series of trepidations and alarms. People feared the consequences of misinterpreting the myths of religion; and they topped their pinnacle of anxiety with a fear of God himself."

"What," I asked timidly, fearing the whiplash of his irony, "what would become of the rash and optimistic hero daring to face the world of today with its furtive fanatics, patriots, gangsters, politicians, exploiters, and robber barons, if he lived a free life, fearing nothing?"

"Jesus is the classic and conclusive answer to that," said he. "But a hero would last longer today, because society, nasty as it is, is not quite so putrid as it was in Jesus' day — thanks to Jesus."

"Then you think," I said, "that people today fall short of the high standard of Jesus' life largely because of cowardice?"

"What else can one think?" replied Bellerophon.

"And," I went on, "this fear that poisons life today is in some measure, you intimate, the consequence of myths built up around the fragmentary biographies of Jesus."

"Incontrovertibly," said he, emphatically.

"In repudiating myth, is there not danger of including — or at least, seeming to include — some valuable truths, such as the existence of God?" I inquired.

"The philosophic mind is not likely to do that," said he. "The mind says: 'How can that be unreal which has created me, unless I, too, am unreal, in which case my thoughts and conclusions are unreal and useless?' Or else it says: 'Which is more likely to be imaginary, this huge universe which the unphilosophic savage experiences in essentially the same way as that in which the most sophisticated modern scholar does, or the ideas which speculative minds, stimulated by hints and analogies and epiphenomenal evidences and the treacherous syllogisms of formal logic, have formulated?' What would be your answer?"

"I should say that the ideas are more likely to be unreal," I replied.

10

"So should I," said he, and continued: "Well, to use a little of this 'treacherous logic,' we might say: If the universe is imaginary, then God must be deceiving me. The alternative may be that God is only what I think. Indeed, he may be only *because* I think. In that case there is no God outside of my mind; and the God of my mind is subject to me — I am not subject to him. But this alternative is practically invalidated by the fact that I did not create myself.

"On the other hand, if the universe is real (a valid supposition since the contrary leads nowhere), then God, the creator, ground, and preserver of it must be real. Hence he is not deceiving me. Hence he and I are not alone. Which means that cooperative search for reality need not be a hopeless task; on the contrary, it has brightest and richest promise."

"I see," said I; "and by these confused syllogisms you escape solipsism."

"What other escape is there?" he asked; and having no reply, I urged him to continue with the myths.

"Possibly I should mention those included under what is called 'special revelation.' The prevailing error in all organized religions has been the supposition that God ever would or could speak to man, that is, reveal himself by verbal communication. Men discover God, or awake to his reality and the manner of his activities, according to their merits and deserts as students of fact and law. For, I repeat, the Creative *Nous* does not reveal himself and his will except in the orderly emergences of his natural world. This 'natural world,' however, includes vast categories in matter, mind, and spirit. The great historic religions and a thousand other puny sects all have claimed that God gave them special truths to cherish and teach. The 'truths' were often as potent and adequate as the authentication and validation of them were top-heavy with presumption and blasphemy."

At this point I interrupted: "If, as you say, God does not speak to man nor interfere with his career, of what utility is prayer? It is evident that men cannot resist the impulse to hope that their cry for help in time of agony or peril will elicit a special providence in their behalf. It has always been a basic article of religious faith. Men have thought that if the gods are of any use, it is in such crises that they can justify their existence. I do not see how you can remove this pillar of orthodoxy with impunity."

"Christopher Wren," replied Bellerophon, "once built an imposing edifice, one important section of which seemed to have inadequate support. The directors complained; so Wren placed two sturdy pillars where support seemed to be required. But he did not let them touch at the top by several inches. However, the directors thought they were touching. It is the same with prayer. Men ought to communicate with the divine Spirit; they ought to meditate upon his laws in a deep awareness of his omnipresence. But the permissible form of verbal worship addressed to the Deity is praise and appreciation.

"Under no circumstances whatsoever ought man instruct God as to human needs or desires; and it is surely brazen presumption to coax for that which God has withheld. Pleas for forgiveness are entirely unnecessary as the soul is purified the instant it turns in true remorse away from its sin."

"But," I injected, "the greatest teachers of all ages have insisted upon prayer in the form of petition."

"It was symbolism, in the age of myth," he replied calmly. "In this age in which men face reality, the soul talks to God as to a great friendly Other, upon whom the soul can depend to respond with all the spiritual machinery of the universe. Prayer is a kind of plugging-in to get and use the eternal and tremendous Power whose dynamos have been storing up energies to last an eternity. Prayer is a tapping of the divine reservoirs of hope, courage, love, and integrity. Prayer ought to be a searching introspection in the presence of God. Man receives from prayer only what he puts into prayer. But that can be a very great deal. God and his universe respond to prayer before it is uttered or thought. One might say: God and his universe are the perpetual answer to all human yearning and aspiration. The child asks for toys; the mature adult asks for nothing; but he finds renewal as his soul finds contact with God."

"Is not man's whole attitude of seeking truth and spiritual assurance a prayer, a solicitation — made the more importunate by his sincerity?" I asked.

"Quite right," said Bellerophon. "It is therefore necessary to keep one's aspirations pure; and it is unnecessary to concentrate the will and emotions upon specific desires. It is certainly superfluous to spend time and energy describing to the Supreme *Nous* the particulars of your ambitions and cravings. Such a thing is dangerous: it savors of selfishness. No one dares covet for himself

12

anything but that which may be shared by all mankind. If a man seeks first of all the ideal of goodness, everything he really needs will come his way; such is the setup of the universe." After a slight pause he continued:

"But a third and still more stagnating class of myths is that which might be called the 'salvation by substitution' myths. These vary greatly. But they all presuppose that the gods have acted as supermen might act. According to this anthropomorphism the gods have to be made propitious or satisfied by human sacrifice. The logical and judicial character of this monstrous idea captured the barbaric imagination of people, especially those of the Graeco-Roman world of the first and second centuries. And, while wholly alien to the spirit and purpose of Jesus' teaching, it has persisted as a stumblingblock to sincere inquirers into this religion, to this day."

"If it is so barbaric," I asked, "why does it persist?"

"Why does war persist? But there is another reason. Not only are men savage and formal, cruel and legal; they are superstitious about a fickle goddess whom they call 'Consistency.' They observed in ancient days that every religion already well-established taught the necessity of sacrifice and atonement. It was an indigenous element in life. Daily routines were replete with repeated exemplifications of this inescapable amenity of social harmony. Today all doctrinaires wish to present to inquirers a system suitable and adaptable to the requirements and tastes of every nation and race the world around. A persuasive claim for missionaries to make is that their religion is a system to which all kinds of people can subscribe since it has elements which satisfy every human curiosity. . . ."

"Well," I interrupted, "what is wrong with that?"

"Only this," he answered: "the proper approach to God is not through an eclectic symbolics agreeable to the majority, but by a faith which trusts the universe and undigressingly seeks and lives by reality."

"But," I replied, "what are the humble, untutored peasants to do? What do they know about 'reality'? Is not religion indispensable to them?"

"Many untutored people have had the profoundest trust in the friendly intentions of God and his universe. And many have possessed an insight into truth and reality as instinctive as the virtues of childhood. The peasant walks by what light he has, with commendable courage, and finds his path growing brighter. We do not

13

expect the peasant to be the discoverer of metaphysical principles. After all, most of religion is practical common sense, brotherliness, and childlike confidence.

"Of course, religion has its profundities. And here is where the philosopher tests his wits. You would not make the intelligence of the peasant the gauge of the philosophic norm in progressive religion, would you? Religious philosophy in its sublimest aspects must be interpreted, if at all, by the disciplined intelligence in its highest reaches. Pure religion does not put a premium upon ignorance. Did men measure the diameter of Antares with first-grade arithmetic? Did men split the atom after a few weeks of high school chemistry? Did the great religions of the Babylonians, Egyptians, Hebrews, and Hindus entrust the formulation of their dogmatic manifestos to groups of simple-minded peasants, who after the day's labors, devoted the fag-end of the day to this easy task of reading the symbols of divine truth in the mysterious depths either of the heavens or of their own fervid imaginations?"

Since he paused here I injected, "To the extent that they did, they made a mess of it."

"Quite true, generally speaking," he said. "Religion in its practical exemplification of goodness and faith is so simple that a child can and does use it. But who is wise enough to know the complete will and intention of the Creative Spirit, or the scope and method of his procedure? Too many mythmakers make their own meagre imagination stand in place of rational application of the surest and highest interpretation of divine purpose. And, therefore, your half-awakened average person is proud to find himself smart enough to be critical of the bungling inefficiency of the ceremonially impressive institutions which claim inspired and infallible authority and sanction. He still loves myth; but he is tired of this ineffectual kind."

"You would include the prophetic myths in this class, I suppose," said I.

"Of course," replied Bellerophon. "And it is astonishing how very plausible the dogmaticians have made the chain of exegetical evidences which has imprisoned pious minds in the orthodox system. They go back to the legend of creation for the first reference to the so-called 'plan of salvation.' The subtle serpent of the garden was called the devil; and he was destined to spoil all of God's splendid work. God's two finest creations go wrong. But instead of correcting the error of Adam and Eve at once and reestablishing

14

the idyllic paradise at the beginning, God allows incalculable misery and agony — incident to the so-called 'fall' — to spread for ages, according to the myth. Then, at length, in answer to men's prayers and in fulfillment of various vague prophecies God sent an adequate sacrifice for the sins of the whole world. I know not which to wonder at more: the art and cleverness with which scholastics have kept this blasphemous myth alive, or the blind credulity of the otherwise fairly rational people who have believed it."

"What," I remarked, "would Jesus have said had he suspected that he would be made a party to such a scheme?"

"It would have added greatly to his burden of sorrows," replied Bellerophon sadly; and after a pause he continued:

"Another class of myths might be named the 'grace of God' myths. The heroes of the saintly days of yore seemed to possess charmed lives. They escaped evils, enjoyed powers, and accomplished their designs in an apparently miraculous manner, by, it was said, the grace of God. And, by the same token, the faithful ones today record escapes from the pits their foes dug for them, from the beguilement of crafty tempters, and from the just recompense of their own willfulness, by the same grace of God. The grateful saint, seeing a sinner plunging into ruin and disgrace, breathes a pious thanksgiving and says: 'There, but for the grace of God, go I.'"

"Well," said I, "is that so monstrously reprehensible? After all, can one help realizing he has escaped certain common catastrophes, and ought he attribute his escape entirely to his own ingenuity and merit?"

"Hear the special pleader!" laughed Bellerophon. "Know this, O man, you escaped what you richly deserved by the grace of your own wit and chance and the natural constitution of your material environment."

"Oh! so you do not admit any part of what we men over on the Earth called 'special providence,'" said I.

"The 'grace of God,'" he answered, "if you insist upon that term, should be confined to one category of divine providence, namely, that in which the superior elements of human equipment and the distinctly spiritual potentialities are augmented beyond philosophic expectation and scientific explanation. We observe this in beauty, in value, in spiritual nobility, in love, in genius, and in the sublimities of human emotion and imagination, as well as in the emerging newness and increasing complexity and significance of the ceaseless creativeness of nature.

"It is a kind of long-range teleology, by the law of which, things seemingly take care of themselves and conspire to provide what is needful for abounding careers for all the creatures which nature brings to life. Such a provision is vastly deeper than human understanding and imagination. It is the concrete form of divine love. It is the all-sufficient evidence upon which to base the hope of finding the universe friendly to the core."

"And yet," I rejoined, "you think this divine love has not the power to come to the rescue of private individuals, to dispense personal piecemeal providences when calamity threatens or failure looms in the offing."

"Your surmisal is quite correct," said he. "Deity does not violate his own decrees. There is no need; eventually the highest and best integration will be established. Some individuals suffer temporal eclipse and apparent ruin, even as the small trees of a forest which are choked and stunted by the giants around them. Many brilliant lights are snuffed out before they reach the maximum of their powers. But the teleology which provided their existence *can,* possibly I should say *must,* also provide the proper eventual sequence. It may be in an intensity of experience which compensates for lack of extensity. Or, it may be in a new experience hereafter in the ocean of universal mind and spirit. We must not forget that we are parts of the divine Mind. Nor, ought we to forget that the light of genius which fails here may be rekindled even more brilliantly to enlighten mankind elsewhere. In short, and to change the figure, an object moves forward in a straight line when set in motion, unless deflected or stopped by an external object. Man moves forward with God's momentum in him. I doubt whether any external force will permanently deflect him."

"How," I asked, "can a man *worship* if he does not expect God to grant his proper requests, most of which concern his well-being and security in body, spirit, and estate?"

"Worship is never real," explained Bellerophon, "except when it is the overflow of the soul in inexpressible adoration. Plainly, this cannot be reduced to ritual and ceremony, to words and music! Artificial stimuli to emotional ecstasy in religion is an escape, futile and dangerous. You do not worship God when you piously fold your hands, bend your knees, close your eyes, and repeat euphuistic laudations, or appeals born of agony and despair. You worship when in utter sincerity of soul you feel a gratitude and reverence and expansion of being which compel you to ascend to a higher plane of living. Lucky is the man who can thus truly worship God once a year during his life!"

"We seem to be wandering from the subject," I observed.

"Not at all," said Bellerophon emphatically. "One of the most dangerous myths in the churches is that which teaches that God delights in formal services, genuflections, offertories, ceremonials, symbolizations. It is not mysterious rituals and sacred festivals that increase righteousness and please God; it is the contrite heart and honest mind."

"You must admit," I said, "that there are some beautiful legends and helpful myths based on the traditional lives of saintly Christian heroes."

"I admit nothing," said Bellerophon, plainly irritated. "You gild these heroes in youthful associations, and they glow warmly and sweetly," he continued, mixing his metaphors badly. "But the pagan Greek loved his Olympic myths just as much, and he found elements which the pagan in spirit to this day find appealing to their classic taste and disposition above the Christian traditions and myths."

"You yourself prefer the Greek myths?" I asked.

"All myths are anathema," he said quietly, and picked up a book as a signal that he was weary of the discussion. But after a pause he added: "The philosophic mind has little time for anything but reality."

Hardly hoping for further comment, I nevertheless asked one more question: "You consider the universe deaf to the mystic longings of man?"

"Nonsense!" he exclaimed, and put down his book. "The universe is overwhelmingly spiritual. The divine overflows everywhere in creation. Just as activity characterizes that which is alive, so emerging purpose and ascending transformation characterize that which is of God. The sensitive soul is aware of this because God wants him to be aware of it. Have you been picturing animal contentment, physical ecstasy, and the prideful glory of social and political preeminence as the goals of life? The universe says to you: 'What now, busy little fellow; look into thy soul and read aright thine instincts.' For these feel not only pall and disgust with the

17

world, but also they feel an urge toward spiritual realization. And these instincts know that there is no frustration in the spiritual realm. So, when failure crushes one's life, nature says to the soul: 'Be of good cheer; God hath planted within thee the power to overcome the world. The kingdom of truth is within thee; live in it, and find inspiration in its supernal realities and its permanent values!'

"That is religion — a constant reference to that quality in the intelligence which is aware of the perfect and the eternal."

As I walked away, wondering what could take the place of exploded myths as an authority and as a ground for the hope of reward for virtue and faith, Bellerophon, as if he had read my thoughts, called after me:

"Goodness is the principal thing; therefore cultivate it. Goodness is religion in action. It must be founded on intelligence and spirituality, not on any supposed supernatural or miraculous pronouncements, nor because of any Plutonian threats or any paradisaical inducements. Goodness must be understood and practiced simply because it is the efficient summation of all the virtues, the all-embracing requirement of man's total nature, the irrefragable and inescapable will of God!"

INCIDENT II

IDEAS AND THEIR EFFECTS

*"A healthful hunger for a great idea is the beauty and
blessedness of life," said Jean Ingelow. The pages of
history reveal how the ideas which have enriched human
life, seemed to come to earnest thinkers just when the
world needed them most. Ideas are more potent than
atom bombs. They who can distinguish the great and
salutary ideas from the base and corrupting, shoulder
the heavy responsibility of implementing the good and
thwarting the bad ones. A second "dark age" will begin
when too few leaders can entertain serious ideas of
world betterment.*

Strolling aimlessly along the west bank of the Styx, I came upon
three notables in animated discussion — Archimedes, Roger Bacon
and Leonardo da Vinci. It is permissible to listen to anyone who is
speaking in this delightful region; for there are no secrets, nor any
need to conceal opinions or appraisals of personal character.
Everyone wears his heart on his sleeve, and reveals his temper and
judgment — whether good, bad or neutral — in his attitude or
utterance, quite involuntarily.

Well, as a matter of fact, we do the same, back on the Earth.
Expressions of dislike, disapproval or scorn, or of any unkind comment and jealous criticism — are quite unnecessary. Casual contacts
with our contemporaries reveal the prevailing affectations, dis-
semblings and the indoctrinated opinions in our minds, without
verbal betrayal. But, on the Styx, the inner thoughts and ruling
passions shout aloud, above the spoken words!

"Man is the only creature that is interested in abstractions"
declared Archimedes, drawing a geometric figure in the sand with
his finger. "He enjoys toying with ideas. He has unbounded con-

19

fidence in his logic, and in the validity of mathematical, technological and chemical symbols. There is not a category of human thought and activity in which Man does not continually explore for useful, needful, valuable and interesting *ideas* — in philosophy, theology, history, archeology, science, exploration, geology, astronomy, and, (in recent times) in nuclear physics, medicine, sociology, law, government, economics, literature, music and art!"

"When psychology began to be a popular topic of conversation," remarked Roger Bacon, "the observation became current that 'some people talk about *things,* some about *people,* and a few about *ideas.'* The invidious implication was, that most people were incapable of discussing abstract subjects, and found their absorbing interest in tangible objects, or, their neighbors and the people whose names appeared in the newspaper headlines. This dilettante assumption was unkind and unjust; for, some of the most important ideas on record have to do with things and their relation to people, their lives, and the quality of their characters — also with places and material circumstances. These factors often determine the very survival of human beings."

"In short," interjected Leonardo, "Man must master his environment and make it sustain him; and this requires the conception of ideas, and the rational and practical discernment of their utility — if we want to have a habitable world and tolerable society.

"Of course, too many adults retain the playfulness of immature years, and give disproportionate attention to trifles and the satisfaction of the five senses. Then, too, many are over-concerned about other people's activities. Experienced craftsmen in modern chemical and electrical laboratories know how important it is to have sure, steady control of every movement, and a perfect correlation of eye and hand. But few people train and discipline their minds as carefully as they do their eyes and hands! Charles Darwin has made the observation that: 'The highest possible stage of moral culture is to recognize that we ought to control our thoughts!' And Pascal, the eminent mathematician and mystic, wrote: 'Man holds an inward talk with himself alone, which it behooves him to regulate well!'

"But, after all, we are by Nature gregarious; it is necessary to be aware of one's social surroundings. To give any attention to things or to people, requires the employment of ideas about them. And our ideas are usually appraisals of their quality — the impressions

20

they make upon our senses and sensibilities. Are they normal or abnormal, competent or incompetent, safe or unsafe? and, have they a justifiable purpose in the scheme of things? In short, are they assets or liabilities in human society? From the dawn of geologic history to the present, there has been a constant purpose in Nature, evidenced by a process of evolutionary mutation; and whenever purpose was not defeated by too great obstacles, progress was made toward stability, utility and adaptability. But whether successful or not, there was always purpose back of its activity. The elements inside the atoms have had it; the molecules have had it; the living cells have had it; and mankind has had it most conspicuously!"

At this point a group of scholars who had been listening to Charles Darwin, Alfred Russell Wallace, Herbert Spencer and Jean de Lamarck, joined us. Among them I noticed Phillips Brooks, Christopher Marlowe, Nathaniel Hawthorne, Romain Rolland, Voltaire, Peter Kropotkin and Horace Walpole. From another direction came another company of American professional men and women. They were behind me, and I had not noticed them. Evidently they had heard some part — perhaps all — of Leonardo's remarks; for one of the women spoke, reminding us of the fact that the permanence of a purpose or an instinct in society to aspire to higher conditions did not always result in the realization of the hoped-for objective.

She named the failure of the American Government to adequately implement the Volstead Act to enforce the Eighteenth Amendment of the Constitution, as a shameful example of the concessions, which upright citizens and their chosen public officials too often make, to the determined degenerates who have defied the law of the nation — in this case, by smuggling and illicitly manufacturing intoxicating liquors. "There can be," she said, "no exoneration nor extenuation of official and social guilt, by the claim that the flood of violations was so rapid and extensive as to be beyond control before the Government could act. It is a major blot upon the Nation's escutcheon, that, to appease the sub-normal, malfeasant elements, and those devotees of 'personal liberty' who assume respectability, yet scoff and sneer at the notion of sympathy and concern for the victims of alcoholism — the citizens of the mightiest nation in the world, repealed, by popular vote the Amendment for Prohibition, in the year 1933 of this so-called civilized era."

There was silence as token of respect for the speaker. But the general sentiment, I felt, was regret that she had used that particular incident in history, to illustrate the recognized contingency that great expectations and noble aspirations do sometimes fall short of desired results. It was Walpole who returned our thoughts to Leonardo's suggestions, and developed them further.

"When we find a human being without a sense of purpose," he said, "we are shocked. Purposelessness is simply a living death. The ideas of purpose can be good or bad. The natural laws will operate in either case. Noble purposes are always a blessing, whatever the outcome. Man's noblest characteristics — honor, generosity, compassion, self-control, love of truth — are not derived from the food he eats, nor are they floating in the air he breathes. Rather, they are the consequences of the ideas he digests, and the purposes he executes.

"The mystery of the source, nature and obvious power of these spiritual Forces in the mind, challenges the interest and inquisitiveness of every vigorous intelligence. There is a secular sophistry — a worldly policy of static materialism — which drains the spiritual meaning out of every thing it touches. Amiel, apropos of this, wrote in his Journal:

'The test of every system is the man it forms. If a system injures the intelligence, it is bad; if it injures the character, it is vicious; if it injures the conscience, it is criminal.'

"Man lives by the constant energizing and vitality of those ideas which we call 'divine.' And, we so term them, because, nothing in Man could have originated them."

Peter Kropotkin, the Russian naturalist and geographer, had been listening with eager interest. He spoke animatedly.

"I have observed," he began, "that ideas related to love, pity, mutuality, self-sacrifice — are absolutely essential to life in this world we have recently left. Even the dumb creatures of forest and field obey the instinct to aid and protect each other. Animals and men who defy this law written upon their hearts, perish as individuals, and as communities! So, an inquiry into the wise use of ideas involves not only self-examination, but an attentive survey of the age-old and world-wide ideas and purposes of all classes and conditions of people. As Matthew Arnold very succinctly expressed it: 'Culture is knowing the best that has been thought, said, and done, in the world.'

"Some attempts have been made to classify the ideas which ought to govern human society. In America, the 'Harvard Classics' — President Charles William Eliot's 'Five-Foot Shelf,' was an effort to supply the best literary aid to culture. Many excellent Encyclopedias are available to enlighten the reader regarding events, conditions and locations of people and things on the Earth, and some of the partly solved mysteries of the infinite space through which Man and his Earth are plunging at an incredible speed!

"It is generally recognized that when people hold sane, reasonable concepts, and cherish the hope and intention of elevating their standards, the consequences will be progressively compensatory and meliorative. The good becomes excellent; the excellent becomes glorious! Hence, the value of studying the character of the ideas that have motivated mankind's conduct. . . ."

I think Kropotkin would have spoken longer; but Nathaniel Hawthorne took advantage of a pause, and remarked:

"To err is human; and the past has revealed more cause to make Man ashamed than to make him glow with pride. However, not all of the past has been inglorious, bungling frustration. Consider the structural magnificence of Man's art! — its beauty, splendor, immensity! And then, reflect that every towering structure with its ornamented exterior and brilliantly decorated interior, and its cloud-kissing pinnacles and domes — in every great city of the ancient and modern world — was once *nowhere* but in the infinitely minute brain-cells of talented men who had *ideas,* and who brought the ideas to a tangible, utilitarian and beautiful realization!

"Is it not a miracle that from an invisibly small cell in the brain of Pericles could have come the splendor of the Athenian Acropolis? Well, it is a wonder many times repeated: in the cathedrals of Europe, the pyramids of Egypt and Yucatan, the Taj Mahal, the Potala in Lhasa of Tibet, the Hindu temple towers of Mandura, the one-time splendor of Karnak, Baalbek and Palmyra, the lofty sky-scrapers of New York City, and the great San Francisco bridge!"

Romain Rolland had walked over near Hawthorne, who at this point invited him to speak. I had enjoyed this French writer's

23

works so much that I was eager to hear what he would contribute to this discussion.

"No one can foresee the future of an idea," he began. "Some superior Cro-Magnon man invented a raft, or hollowed a log, in order to convey himself across some river or lake; and he used a paddle for propulsion. Someone, perhaps the same fellow, thought of a sail. Rival inventors made bigger and better boats. The boats grew into ships — small at first, but after a while, with two and three banks of oars, and huge sails. The present day ocean liners are floating palaces, equipped with every latest invention for comfort and luxury.

"The story of modern science is the fascinating march of ideas, stimulated by imagination, and validated by experiment. The same development has taken place in art. The drawings and sculpture of primitive men who felt the urge to illustrate what they had seen, twenty or thirty thousand years before the present era, are rather crude, and give but faint promise of the glories which were to come — in, for example, the masterpieces of Greece and Italy. An amazing approach toward perfection in art in both Greece — in the Periclean Period — and, in Italy — in the Medicean Period, lifted art to the zenith of excellence in taste, refinement, charm and beauty. Earthlings today and tomorrow are not likely to see any works of chisel or brush superior to the Laocoon, the Venus de Milo, the Doryphorus (or spear-bearer) of Polycletus, the Moses, David and Pieta of Michelangelo, and the paintings of Raphael, Rubens, Titian, Nicolas Poussin, Andrea del Sarto. However, the many artists of the past century are, in some cases, only a short step below the illustrious masters. The significance of the art idea could engage us indefinitely.

"It is difficult to appraise the value of *any* idea. Edmund Burke's 'Conciliation' had little or no effect upon British diplomacy. At the Centennial World's Fair, in America, Alexander Graham Bell's 'telephone' was laughed at as a clever but useless toy! History relates that Columbus had many humiliating repulses, before he obtained funds and backing for his fate-laden voyage across the Atlantic. Pythagoras, about 450 years before the present era, believed that the Earth revolved around the Sun; but many martyrs died before the idea was finally accepted as the true astronomical concept.

"All prophetic originators of great ideas seem to 'live before their

24

time.' Leonardo da Vinci's ideas of a 'flying-machine,' and of canal-locks for putting ships on a different level, were ignored in his day, and not tried for hundreds of years. But good ideas, no matter how unwelcome, have a way of surviving. There was that predilection persisting in the hearts of the English Barons in 1215 which drove them to compel King John to sign the Magna Charta — an idea which again found its illustrious expression in the American colonists' 'Declaration of Independence.'

"Poetry, song and drama have celebrated the heroic struggles of adventurous pioneers and migrating groups and nations, to procure and secure habitable lands, peace, and national sovereignty. They are the thrilling stories of exiles, pilgrims, non-conformists and freedom-loving seekers of Arcadia, Utopia, Shangrila. . . . And all thoughtful persons are better for knowing these 'soldiers of fortune,' who have been inspired by the fascination of an *idea*: the idea of a great newness, and the hope that therein they will find self-realization and the good life! Yes; there would be no civilization — because there would be no historic progress, without men of ideas!"

I noticed that Disraeli was on the point of interrupting Rolland several times. He now spoke, with his usual earnestness and deliberation.

" 'As a man thinks — so is he'; and, as a nation thinks — so is it. Clearly, there are various kinds of ideas. Some are frankly corrupt, provocative of debasing passions, perilous to sanity, conducive to self-indulgence and moral turpitude. In contrast, many ideas are ennobling, spiritualizing and transforming. Between these extremes there are many shades of ideas, neutral or indifferent, palliative and tolerating by policy, or concerned with subjects which have no ethical reference nor moral connotations. Conservative, respectable, luke-warm citizens deal in this impartial brand of ideas. They live safe. They do not invite trouble. They live in the 'average man's world' — and revere the status quo. They are colorless and usually very exasperating.

"Unfortunately many nations back on the Earth have suffered what might be called a plague of schizophrenia. Consider the early Hebrew tribes, led by Moses out of Egypt into the Arabian deserts. These Israelites had been under a cruel bondage too long. All ambition and racial pride had seeped away. They wanted merely to live; and now they yearned for the flesh-pots of Egypt. Evidently, also, they missed the mysterious rites and spectacular pageantry of the Egyptian polytheism. Moses was barely able to recapture the rapidly fading concept of the One God Whom their patriarchs had worshiped.

"The spiritual atmosphere of medieval Europe was murky, morbid, depressing and ominously premonitory. The laws of State and Church were cruel and unjust. Life was too overloaded with misgivings and forebodings, for most people, to find, amid their struggles to keep alive, much innocent pleasure, natural joy, love and high aspiration.

"Paganism had shot its bolt and was rapidly being forgotten. But many of its superstitions had crept into the Christian Church. The few intelligent people who had high and happy ideas and progressive predilections were afraid to express them. Governments governed by fear; and the Church backed the rulers by teaching that those in authority were ordained by God, and must be obeyed. Instead of instilling a reverential love for the Deity, there was an emphasizing of the idea that 'The fear of the Lord is the beginning of wisdom.'

"Demonism was a great mental scourge; and it still mars the peace of society here and there. It was a deeply planted belief in the actual existence of a personal, autonomous author and producer of evil, called Satan, or the Devil. He was elevated to the dignity of a god, and made a rival of the benevolent Creator. The ignorant and superstitious (and their name was 'Legion') in many cases felt that innocent living was an impossible attainment, with demonic powers constantly coercing them to choose evil instead of good. A sense of personal responsibility was difficult enough to sustain without such an obtrusive encumbrance.

"The chronicles of mankind show clearly that the idea of a calm security and a confident anticipation of its continuance, is the only provocative idea that is certain to motivate and support peace, progress, prosperity and liberty, socially — and happiness, character, genius and high achievement, personally!"

Voltaire was always partial to the English: and here on the Styx he renewed his pleasant associations with the friends he had made during his three years' exile in England — Sir Thomas More, Addison, Bolingbroke, Swift and Steele and others. He listened with evident pleasure to Disraeli, and now, very much in the spirit of his one-time nonconformity, took up the theme.

"Along with this specious orthodoxy," he said, "which the Earl of Beaconsfield has mentioned, went the further futility which solemnly postulated, on the authority of Paul, Augustine, Luther, and Calvin, that some individuals were chosen (some say before the supposed 'fall of Adam' — others say after) by the Creator, to receive eternal felicity with Him in His celestial realms, while others were marked for endless misery.

"No pagan Nemesis, no remorseless Fate, could so miserably have confused the minds and depressed the spirits of mankind! This predestinational notion had its roots in the dogma-of-convenience called 'the literal inspiration of Scriptures.' The Church said to sinners: 'You must believe the words of Scripture, and the doctrines of the Church; and you must observe all prescribed rites and formalities — or be anathematized, outcasts here and hereafter!' The Church failed to say (at least with adequate emphasis and frequency): 'You must reverence Life, Goodness, Purity, Mercy, Truth, and Love — for the Creator has written this law of His upon your hearts!'

"Recall the hedonistic dereliction prevailing everywhere in medieval Europe. Will Durant has intimated the sodden, bestial debauchery of the society of that period, in his historic volume 'The Renaissance.' Machiavelli frankly advocated mendacity and ambiguity as a prudent policy in statecraft. Yet in that era of flagrant dissipation there lived some amazing intellects and admirable characters — men who were motivated by different and very superior ideas — poets, thinkers, saints and artists. Savonarola, scholar, orator and reformer, was burned at the stake for having too much influence over the people. Leonardo da Vinci, the prodigiously versatile genius, managed to escape martyrdom, and left his valuable ideas for succeeding generations to develop and use."

I saw Leonardo smile and move his head negatively, disclaiming the encomium. Voltaire continued:

"Michelangelo, the incomparable master of art, managed to keep his person out of the clutches of the heresy-hunters; and so did Raphael Sanzio, the modest, amiable and wonderful artist. Bruno, man of profound insight, was less fortunate. He was too intelligent for his age; and after seven years of cruel imprisonment, was burned at the stake. Galileo, the courageous star-gazer, dared to contradict Aristotle and Thomas Aquinas; but in his old age,

27

weakened, and rescued himself from the fiery vengeance of the inquisition by a lie.

"The course of history is seen to be that which results from the conflict of ideas, good and bad. The constructive and transforming ideas seem to live longer and to achieve more of a change than the false and destructive ideas — for which we must be thankful!"

Benjamin Franklin, with several of his French admirers, had joined the assembly while Rolland had been speaking. Voltaire now greeted him and urged him to add his thoughts upon the theme of 'ideas.' Thus importuned, he smiled genially, and after a slight pause, began:

"Back on Earth we were never as conscious as we ought to have been, of the tremendous power and significance of 'ideas.' We could not presage the damage of wrong ideas, nor realize the possible value and blessing of right ones. It is difficult to understand why the septic decay, which so many false and baneful ideas produced in medieval society, did not spread increasingly and overwhelm mankind in phrenic neuroses! However, when mental and moral devastation was at its maximum, a change occurred. The progress in intellectual and spiritual evolution began to accelerate once more, as a happy result of the 'revival of learning' with the help of the intelligence and science of the Arabian Mohammedans, and of the revolutions in France and America.

"Ideas which held a virtuous vitality were, at last, free to all. The value and authority of learning, and the scientific understanding of cause and effect, were quickly grasped as essential factors in the creation of the good life.

"The ageless, basic ideas, compounded of fact and reason — ideas that excite men's curiosity regarding the origins of present conditions and tendencies — ideas that prompt doubt and dissatisfaction because some phases of life are not ideal — ideas that discern injustice in social or economic methods, or inadequacy and futility in results — and, the ideas that persuade the soul to desire the highest, the truest and the best: *these* are the potent and indispensable elements in the acquiring of a mature selfhood! These transform the personality! These imbue the soul with nobility and joy, and give the conscious spirit a wisdom which discerns the realities of existence under their manifold appearances. And, the discovery of reality is the recognition of happiness! Nature wears many masks — lest fatuous fools fail to reverence her."

Franklin paused; and after a few moments of silence, Phillips Brooks, the renowned American divine, spoke briefly.

"Gravitation is a great, universal mystery. In our earthly experience everything was weighted and drawn downward by its incomprehensible power — except the Soul; it could defy the downward pull! It could enjoy the mystery of Levitation! By it a man could 'lift himself by his boot-straps.' He could search his mind and heart and find the inspiration which elevated his being with a transcendent aspiration!

"Ideas of perfection in knowledge, freedom and mutuality — ideas of the golden age of peace and brotherhood — ideas of absolute integrity, purest love and spiritual achievement — such ideas are those which Man is constitutionally equipped to understand, desire, and use, for his continual conquest of Truth, and his completion of mature Selfhood!

"Jesus enshrined in a lucid and supernal precept the ideal of human destiny: Liberation from the thraldom of evil ideas: 'Ask, seek, knock . . . and you shall know the Truth, and the Truth shall make you free!'

"St. Paul, if he were here now, would quote one of his greatest exhortations: 'Whatsoever things — whatsoever ideas — therefore, are true, honorable, just and pure, lovely and of good report — having virtue and deserving praise — *think on these things,*' and your spirit will be happy, high and holy!"

On this lofty note the colloquy ceased, and we drifted apart.

INCIDENT III

MELANIPPIDES ESSAYS HERMENEUTICS

Thoreau in this Incident might have quoted Jesus (Mt. 25:14ff) to support his contention that Deity seems to entrust much of His Kingdom's progress to men. Unfortunately, Churchmen very generally assume that their Theology is the true Religion. They pay but little heed to others' attempts to find greater and nobler truths. Perhaps Jesus' injunction to "Ask, seek and knock" was not addressed to them!

After watching a long game of chess played by Napoleon, the notorious Corsican, and Ben Morey, an American printer, it was a pleasant relaxation to stumble upon a group of celebrities lounging on a grassy knoll about a stone's throw from the west bank of the Styx, discussing anthropology.

I was especially entertained by the dialogue of José Rodó (whose quaint *Proteus* I had always esteemed as a precious literary gem), and Henry Thoreau, the glorifier of personal independence. Among the first words I overheard was the phrase "Deus evanescens," which might be used to designate the subject of the debate. The group of listeners grew as the two plunged deeper into their argument; and many comments were interjected by the interested audience.

The part which clung to my memory and which I have here set down is that which began when the ancient Melian lyric poet Melanippides appeared and was invited to contribute his thought. Thoreau had just voiced the opinion that the cosmic *Nous* seemed to have been preparing men's minds for the realization that he wished to retire from the scene — wished to have men understand that he was going off to a far country and was leaving mankind in charge.

Rodó considered the opinion dated and labeled, and argued that

30

interpretations of divine relationships with earthly inhabitants were always subject to amendment; that if Thoreau had lived in another part of the world, or half a century later, he might have felt that the cosmic *Nous* was making obvious overtures to men to receive him more intimately and cordially as one who desired to take more and more part in the human drama.

Voltaire objected here that the human episode was a comedy, not a drama; and that God does not demean himself by being implicated in such undignified antics.

But Thoreau upheld his thesis and maintained that all history confirmed the theory that the Divine Intelligence had hardly enabled the human mind to arrive at a fairly rational conception of Divinity when he began to withdraw from the imagination of the race. Progressively men's so-called "revelations" were discredited, and their charismatic endowment repudiated, as thinkers discovered all speculations upon, and interpretations of human experience to be inadequate. "Yet, increasingly," said he, "men have found superior satisfaction in knowing that wisdom is to be earned, virtue is to be developed, and beauty is to be produced, by the independent, uncoerced will and energy of mankind."

Somewhere, early in the conversation, Democritus, the philosopher, Sositheus, the tragic poet of Syracuse, and Thomas Paret, the American scholar, made suggestions to the effect that Deity expresses himself only through intelligent minds; and that as minds find themselves they find the mystery of God, and lose sight of him elsewhere. But Thoreau did not think the philosopher ought to lose sight of God in nature, howsoever neutral nature appears to be, and quoted Emerson:

> Enough for thee the primal mind
> That flows in streams, that breathes in wind;
> Leave all thy pedant lore apart
> God hid the whole world in thy heart.

Said Sositheus: "When the Cosmic Energy first crystallized into light and heat, and what the moderns call electrons and atoms, the Divinity back of it infused his life into the very substratum of materiality — injected his essential nature into all creation."

It was not apparent at first which side Melanippides would champion. I recall that he commented ambiguously upon Sositheus' remark by saying that it might be the case that the supreme *Nous* was thus successfully concealing himself from the *uncomprehending* eyes of men. He began by listing the stages of man's misapprehensions of deity. He had spoken only a little while when I saw the great lyrist, Simonides of Ceos, come into the group, with Stesichorus, the choral poet, of Sicily. They took a position just in front of me, and I heard Stesichorus remark: "This is the first time I ever heard Melanippides express himself save in Bacchic doggerel."

"Oh, he wrote some very good things," replied Simonides, "while he was living in Macedonia under the patronage of Perdiccas II. Plutarch likes his lyrics, and gives him a high rank. So does Xenophon. He has quite forsaken Dithyrambus, and is absorbing all the recent philosophy and culture he can find by association with the intellectuals."

Meanwhile, Melanippides had begun a kind of survey of the evolution of the idea of the divine in human society. I had been told that he had become greatly interested in the subject ever since his extensive conversations with the pious Frenchman, Ernest Renan.

"How it came about," said he, "no anthropologist has confidently explained; but in very early times men found themselves believing that a mysterious and invisible power, later termed the *mana*, resided in various congenial phenomena of nature, and exerted an influence upon the environment and even upon the careers and daily lives of men."

"Would you consider this belief in the universal spiritual power residing in natural objects a religion?" someone asked.

"Hardly that," he replied; "just as you do not consider the confused and hazy fancies of a child a valid and sufficient basis for conclusive opinion and action founded on that opinion. To the early races the concept of the *mana*, while an element in the racial ethos, was not a religious value in the modern sense of the term.

"In anthropologic findings it is correct to say, according to Ames, that whatever catches attention may be regarded as a spirit. To the aborigines there is no distinction between history and fiction, and there exists no clear boundary between actuality and dream life, and between perception and imagination. Such relationships as are intimately experienced and are felt to be important are governed by spirits — that is, they are considered to be those that possess the *mana* in the greatest degree.

"Modern examination of the stages in man's comprehension of the world-outside-himself, and, in particular, his concepts of deity, reveals a definite progress toward a hope that the universe is a spiritual affair, that deity is the real summation of all permanent values, and more — the reality supporting goodness, truth, and beauty.

"Very early in man's religious development the shaman or medicine man cultivated both magic and holiness. He achieved first, Havelock Ellis tells us, a notable conquest of his own soul. He tried to enter into a harmony with the universe. By this his sensations and power of apprehension were made sharper. In this unity with the spirit of the world (mysticism, in one form or another), the possibilities of both the control of nature (magic — later science) and the ecstasy of harmony with nature (religion) are introduced into human thought, with, says Ellis, 'a core of reality and an endless trail of absurdity, persisting even into advanced civilization.'

"As an outgrowth of the *mana* concept there came a marked improvement in men's imagination. The spirits became human in form and divine or semidivine in character — not that holiness, or absolute wisdom, or any kind of perfection was ascribed to them, but that they were much more powerful and knowing than men. Early gods of the Semitic and Hellenic races were (as W. Robertson Smith and Gilbert Murray have explained) species of animals. The humanizing and universalizing of gods in Israel and Greece was a significant achievement.

"Polytheism attained a certain culture and poetic beauty in the mythologies of the Far East and North, and reached its zenith in the Olympic council. Here and there a nation enriched and elated by conquests gave its favorite gods the glory; and in many cases one outstanding deity became the ruling god. These tutelary gods shared the fortunes and fame of their worshipers.

"The next stage was a monotheism which ascribed to the deity rule and authority over all the earth. Only the educated held this concept with any degree of consistency. But still the god was patterned over man as a model, and reflected all the immaturity and deep selfishness of his creators.

"A later step up was the concept of a transcendent god. His personality was still quite human; but it was felt that he possessed qualities and attributes humanly inconceivable — that he had purposes quite beyond human ken, and that the puny solar system of which the earth is a small part may be but a remote experimental station, hardly included in the ultimate completion of the cosmic program."

As Melanippides paused, Walt Whitman spoke in his usual direct manner: "I had many companions whose search for God was guided by intellect alone. They reached the stage you have just mentioned. They were honest, serious, unafraid. I loved them. But they did not use their heart. They could not feel the pulse of the world. They would not embody all presences — high and low, good and bad, pure and defiled — to know the warmth of love in their bones and bowels."

"Yes; it is the love expression of the divine through the human that this class has lacked," replied Melanippides. "These intellectuals have not given all of themselves to a total experience of God in the world."

Margaret Fuller and two other New Englanders began to defend the transcendentalists, holding that they had endeavored to accept all realities both intellectually and emotionally. But realizing that the desire was to hear Melanippides, they quickly subsided, and the poet resumed:

"Among various parallel developments of theologic speculation a sort of deism revived, in which God is a detached and disinterested creator of island universes, playing with matter and force and apparently growing tired of his experiments. Or, he is an impersonal force; and this world which men inhabit is the product of a blind fortuitism. Or, he is the human image brought into consciousness and some sort of objective reality by spiritual emergences in collective powers and social values."

"That," remarked Rodó, "sounds like a refinement of the old totem religion in which the god is the spirit of the tribe."

Melanippides hesitated, then remarked: "There are some differences between primitive totemism and the positivism developed by Comte and Ames, and the social religious theories of Durkheim in which religion is the experience of kinship, the mystical expression of the collective spirit of the group. Ames suggests that God is the spirit of human idealism, the living process in which men live and move and have their being. He is a sort of glorified Alma Mater or Uncle Sam, constantly offering appreciable rewards for stated conduct and achievement. But he is as real as man's own nature, and as resourceful as man's inexhaustible aspiration.

34

"To the profound Whitehead, religion is 'world-loyalty,' and God is a non-temporal, actual entity — the principle of concretion, dipolar in nature. By his *primordial* nature he is free, eternal, and unconscious. By his *consequent* nature, originating in created, material worlds, he is determined, incomplete, and conscious. To Leuba, God seems to be an unsolved problem. He said he could not persuade himself that divine personal beings have more than a subjective existence. The naturalism of Santayana and Dewey lead up the same blind alley.

"Reason, as far as we can go under its conduct, compels us to postulate a *limited* creative control. I do not say *finite,* since the limitation is self-imposed and may be local — that is, operative in this tiny corner of the universe only.

"This, then, is a hurried glimpse at the beginning and the present development of artificial theology and religious conviction which have so powerfully influenced the social cultures of mankind — the winds of doctrine which have blown the souls of earnest people from pillar to post.

"Human experience seems to indicate that, as Thoreau has said, this divine latescence is deliberate. The Deity seems to wish to let mankind feel the fullest weight of world-life responsibility, and to let men do the supreme difficulties instead of prayerfully waiting for God to do them. God withdraws, as if expecting the soul of man to adventure more grandly when released from the binding belief in the surveillance of an all-seeing, all-knowing deity. The fear of the Lord may be the beginning of wisdom, but not the conclusion of it."

At this point someone in a group of Anglicans asked: "Could it not be argued that the evolution of religious faith demonstrates the increasing nearness and the fuller revelation of God and his desires, inasmuch as the result of loyalty to indoctrinated faith and the conviction that God is a very present help in time of trouble has been an improvement in the world's civilization and a refinement of man's ethical instincts?"

There was a murmur of dissent to the idea of cultural improvement. When I gave my attention to Melanippides again, he was saying: "Divine patrimony, guardian angels, special providence, mystic visions, fairy godmothers and good-luck charms are childish, but, some think, beautiful products of fancy in an artificial and sheltered society. But the mature soul suffocates in such an at-

35

mosphere. The soul must face facts and overcome the world by its own strength — without Siegfried's Nothung sword, Mambrino's helmet, Aladdin's lamp, or the rabbit's foot.

"The presumption back of a divine patrimony," he continued, "is that the human soul is permanently immature and requires the divine apron strings for perpetual support. This rests on certain familiar analogies by which existence itself seems to be grounded in a divinely established scheme of forces, elements, and laws, and independent existence is shown to be impossible."

"But," insisted Rodó, "nothing is complete, nothing totally autonomous, as you admit. Hence, man, who sums up all the mysteries of mundane existence, is also amenable to laws, and along with everything else in nature is subject to limitations. Does this not virtually place man in the role of a helpless dependent, saved only by the material and particular providences of God who is the ground of man's biologic and psychic being?"

"By those who think God altogether such an one as man is," Melanippides replied, "it is assumed that God does specific miracles, that the machinery of the universe is so devised as automatically and infallibly to set up and carry out poetic justice; so organized as to effect an eventual readjustment of injustice, inequality, and frustration; so planned as to promote material progress and a higher culture, and to reveal more and more the truths which man by his own powers could never discover. It is further assumed that man develops certain spiritual needs which the universe is in duty bound to supply with real, objective satisfactions. It is said that man is kept going by hope; his courage and morale are maintained by faith; his integrity is sustained by the conviction that conscience is a special creation, and that the will of God is supernaturally revealed. Since man's total welfare seems thus involved in his religious convictions, the assumption is that the deity must be, as John Fiske would say, such an one as provides an actual, objective answer to these psychologic requirements.

"Man is truly a helpless dependent in respect to his physical resources. He owes his life and all to the long range providence of God in nature. We can start with man acclimated to this world and its furnishings. The question now is: Must God constantly revise his laws, interfere with nature, and overrule the folly and faulty good intentions of man? Must he perpetually

36

parcel out microscopic justice, mercy, and truth? Must he forever sit in a court of appeals to keep human simpletons from destroying themselves and their civilizations? I say that God has not given us any grounds for thinking that he has so mismanaged his creation."

"Every great historic religion contradicts what you claim," interjected Rodó.

"It may be said, in general," continued Melanippides, "that while every religious system has made claim to *revelations* as the bases of faith, none can offer satisfactory evidence of the authenticity of its 'revelations.' If we could say definitely, Thus spake God! we would have what many consider a certain basis for religious confidence. But, paradoxically, we would have therein the end of religion. The moment the will, intellect, and emotions are deprived of adventurous faith by some coercion, they lose their verve, their creative urge, their spiritual independence. The overt effects are standardization, creed making, conservatism, persecution.

"The soul needs to venture, needs to explore, to search — to ask, seek, knock. Faith — in the sense of confidence that an appropriate emergence will follow the right effort — is necessary to the healthy condition of the soul. Certainty is soporific. Doubt is the matrix of thought. Both science and religion face the same paradox: The more thorough your search, the less sure is your knowledge. The sincerity that asks difficult questions creates exceptional integrity and spiritual efficiency. A sanely critical attitude has been the first move toward every advance in human welfare in all the history of the world.

"Moses, Isaiah, Lao-tse, Buddha, Jesus, Spinoza felt the spiritual powers of the universe vividly. It matters not how they interpreted these feelings — in what categories and vocabularies — the great fact is that they felt them, and that their feeling is measurably reproducible. It was faith, in every case, not certainty — at least not that absolute, dead-weight fact-knowledge which silences the senses, judgment, imagination, reason, and intellect. Loosely speaking, the emergences in human minds of the selfsustaining truths by which men ought to live have been called *religious values*. Very good — so long as we understand how and why."

Some seventeenth-century scholar asked several unnecessary

37

questions, and asserted that any truth felt strongly in the heart was the "word of God." Melanippides was very patient. He replied: "The good, true, and beautiful are the divine goals for man. That is as far as I will go. Too many sects have claimed a monopoly upon the 'word of God.' It has been characteristic of religious organizations that in every epoch their doctrinaires have denounced and rejected what had been confidently affirmed in the preceding epochs as immutable and incontrovertible.

"The development of the idea of God in the Hebrew race is typical. Elohim (literally *the gods*) or Jehovah, as he was called by some, is represented at first as a whimsical, arbitrary creator, who allows his finest creation to go to ruin in irrational anger over a trifling disobedience to a meaningless command — a denouement which in his omniscience he was supposed to have anticipated! He is next a lawgiver, thundering out of Mt. Sinai. Soon he is a god of war, leading his chosen people through a wilderness, to harden them for conflict and conquest. He is a tribal god who hates the multitude of nations whose people do not worship him. He is a cruel god, who asks a devoted people to do hideous crimes in the name of religion. He is a capricious and irresolute god, who sends one unsuccessful prophet after another to be stoned by jeering mobs. He is a vindictive god, who sends scourges upon the unappreciative sinners who will not be impressed by the picayune miracles of his messengers.

"The deity postulated by Jesus and a few of his forerunners among the prophets was different. Love, mercy, truth, and progress had become such conspicuous values that men of spiritual insight must needs attribute these qualities to God, the source of all good.

"But the Ecclesia Christiana was soon falling into the age-old anthropomorphism. It continued the Hebrew error of importuning God for personal gifts, favors, health, prosperity. Soon it presented God as one to be revered (if one would save his soul) as a Trinity, and as one who must be approached in the strict observance of orthodox ritual. God was to be served by the mortification of the flesh and deeds of supererogation. He was one to be glorified by victory of arms, as in the crusades; to be magnified by the torturing and slaying of heretics; to be propitiated by a proper appreciation of his redeeming grace and by a true understanding of the intricate doctrines of incarnation and atonement, sacraments and penance, *communicatio idiomatum,* and eschatology. He was held as one who had put his final will and testament in sixty-six various booklets, every word of which had its value by virtue of being literally inspired by the Spirit of God himself. At length he is a deity indifferent to man's theological vagaries, but one who demands observance of respectable morals and a loyal support and defense of the *status quo*. Moreover, through every stage it has been assumed that God holds within him a demoniac quality, in amazing contrast to his love and compassion; for, he is said to be capable of consigning to everlasting agony those whom he has not seen fit to equip with intelligence and strength of moral will adequate to resist sin.

"No student of history dares point to any past, orthodox appraisal and say: 'That represents the truth concerning the deity!' It would be a bold conservative who would point to the annals of the church militant with its persecutions, its compromises with paganism, and its surrenders to the world, and say: 'Behold the finger of God in history! Behold the saving grace of the Almighty!' "

As Melanippides paused here, Rodó inquired: "Are we to suppose that God would remove himself beyond the reach of the human heart without helping men to agree upon some approximate idea of his nature, his will, his purpose — without leaving some reliable, redeeming intellectual gift, some cogent, convincing indorsement of the true values in life?"

"But," responded Melanippides, "has he not been doing this through the ages by making man a rational and spiritual being? True gifts and permanent values are not corpuscular and sensory; they are spiritual. The geologic earth is an amazing ball — but not the sphere of man's truest glory and elevation. Plainly the old globe isn't going to roll pleasantly into some external paradise, some dream-fulfilling port of heart's desire, for the happy solution of all man's problems. Whatever men learn of truth and God and happiness they have to work out for themselves. There are ample quantities of tools and raw materials.

"More than that, God has infused his life into his creatures — has, indeed, injected the vital force of his essential nature into the whole substratum of materiality."

Cotton Mather spoke at this juncture: "You have reminded us that recent formulations of the concept of God pay but scant heed

to the orthodox doctrines relating to divine and miraculous interference in men's careers. But I must remind you that the miracle of
nature is a constant factor; and in nature there are calamities and
scourges and woes. Was it not a part of the divine plan that peril,
pain, and privation should persist, so that men would be prompted
to appeal to heaven — in short, to keep men interested in God
and conscious of their dependence? One of your greatest poets in
modern times, Robert Browning, writes:

"And, all day, I sent prayer like incense up
To God the strong, God the beneficent,
God ever mindful in all strife and strait,
Who, for our own good, makes the need extreme,
Till, at last, He puts forth might and saves."

"By no means," exclaimed Melanippides with considerable feeling, "can I assent to such a sentiment. Reverence for the divine
integrity is shocked by hearing that 'man's extremity is God's opportunity.'"

But Cotton Mather continued his demur. "To the loss of
miracle," said he, "and the implied indifference of God to the de-
vastating catastrophes suffered by men, must be added the shock of
realizing that all history has taken place under the delusion of a
fancied divine support, and all human effort has depended upon
supposed but 'impossible' miracles for faith and hope. Has man
been blind? And do you ask me to believe that in this supposed
blindness he has built a vast ecclesiastical system, fostered a great
civilization, and found peace in the consciousness of God's favor?"

To which Melanippides replied: "Yes! And this blindness has
been responsible for misery and frustration, the pain of which his
cherished illusions and mistaken faith only partially alleviated. Just
as the human mind awoke to the startling fact that the earth does
not rest like a huge convex shield on a tortoise, but revolves like a
ball, and spins around the sun, so the mind has to awake to the
fact that mysterious unknown laws hold the destiny of mankind in
an orbit, at the centre of which is that illuminating essence or
principle which we call intelligent, purposeful love.

"Here are new and unformulable laws in vast, teleological ges-
tation, selecting out of the comprehensive phenomena of the

40

creative flux the good, true, and beautiful elements as permanent values."

Walter Raleigh interrupted: "But men are not educated to appreciate permanent values. And, if they are convinced that no all-seeing eye is watching them, they will descend to all manner of concupiscence. Does not the denial of a justice-dispensing deity in time and in eternity make one a nullifidian? Was the faith of our fathers all wrong?"

Before Melanippides could speak, Walt Whitman replied to him. "If a man holds a religion," said he, "and is loyal to it because an austere arbiter is watching him, that man's religion is vain and vicious, and his loyalty dishonorable. The very humblest men instinctively learn of sincerity and kindness and other 'permanent values.'"

Francis Asbury spoke: "Why," he asked, "cannot the Creator provide for man's exigent emergencies, just as he provides for his generic requirements?"

"I thought we had covered that point," said Melanippides. "It is because the purpose of evolution is to achieve for those of the highest intelligence the greatest amount of free choice possible. Also, because a minute, detailed, piecemeal supervision of individual careers by the cosmic Mind would set up laws annulling great basic principles of integration. For, evolution is a process through the millennia of ages, in which is introduced a purging principle of test and fining, deliberately to produce gold in the bosoms of both men and mountains. Such is the most probable reading of nature's cryptogram. But, mark well, man must mine that gold himself and alone!

"This gold is refined from the ores of goodness, beauty, and truth. These basic values are the supreme elements in the adequate beneficence of God. They are the substantial qualities of his being; and as such they become the spiritual realities in man. Epictetus wrote: 'What is the essence of God? Mind, Intelligence, Reason? True; here, then, look for the essence of the good.'"

It was at this point that someone asked Melanippides how the saint of the future would surpass the saint of the past. Several scholars, including Abelard, Duns Scotus, Thomas Higginson, Hugo Grotius, Leibnitz and my friend Paret, discussed sainthood at some length. Finally, I noticed that Melanippides was speaking again. He was saying:

41

"Often the saints of old caught a clearer vision of reality, but they were generally confused by a conviction that they owed a loyalty to the traditions and forms under which the popular and familiar religious values were usually given expression. There was no science, and there was no adequate philosophy as yet to delocalize their apperceptions. They still considered God an opportunist; they still believed in the possibility of divine partiality.

"The saint of the future needs not be disturbed by traditions nor inhibited by superstitions. He will see but one *miracle:* the universal law of accelerated value in all being, in all life, in all virtuous and purposeful achievement. He will see but one *providence:* the creation-long teleology, by which the self-effacement of a Jesus, a Socrates, a Spinoza, can be traced back to the conditions which ten million years before made possible the feeble self-control of a Silurian polyp. He will see but one *creation:* the continuous procession of the unseen and eternal into the life of the world. The visible universe — as George Santayana says, in substance — must be constructed upon some general and all-embracing principle, which our philosophy and our senses must discover before we can know how to find the unseen and eternal world of which this universe is the emanation.

"The saint of the future will know but one *moral principle:* the preservation of integrity — an integrity which tolerates no injustice and secret selfishness in his own life. He will recognize but one *religion:* the ethical conduct of life, which means the conscious loyalty to idealism and the constant awareness of the categorical imperatives of duty to the race and duty to one's own highest conceptions of constructive living.

"And, the saint of tomorrow will know only one *God:* the cosmic spirit whose life operates in distant Ursa and the Pleiades as well as in the protoplasmic structure of the smallest animalculum — whose purposes include the burning and cooling of a billion suns as well as the functioning of a billion reflex arcs in the human brains in which mentality and character are evolving — a God whose grace and power may be appropriated by human spirits who live as intelligent and free exponents of the good, true, and beautiful. Emerson says: 'As a plant upon the earth, so a man rests upon the bosom of God; he is nourished by unfailing fountains, and draws at his need inexhaustible power.'

"Hidden and mysterious as ever, more remote than men have

42

imagined, yet more wise and loving in long term providence than human intellect can fully understand, this God radiates his power and spirit and being into the life and mind of man. And the rationalizing genius of man responds and, like the heliotrope, turns and faces the source of light.

"Vastly removed, yet closer than breathing and hands and feet, God recedes still farther away, yet comes still closer to the heart of man!"

Melanippides paused so long that we thought he had concluded; and Walt Whitman remarked: "I am reminded that the great comrade Jesus, whom men revered as if he were a god, on whom his beloved friends leaned all too heavily, on whom I leaned across the centuries — that he saw how greatly he dominated the wills of his friends, and that he said it was expedient for them that he go away."

The ancient lyrist nodded to Whitman and resumed: "The mature saint of tomorrow will learn to depend upon his native powers, his intuitions and spiritual impulses, his inventiveness and the secrets he discovers in nature and society and his own heart's experience. He will use his findings — having a new, sure faith in their validity — to build a world independent of schools and creeds and traditions. The best of the past he will utilize as a forester uses dry lumber to feed his winter fire.

"The future saint will not cry to God in consternation of doubt or fear of death or agony of grief. He will feel that every experience, howsoever painful, unexpected, or unmanageable, is his share of the pulsating life of a God-saturated universe, in which all things tend to work together for the eventual triumph of the good, true, and beautiful, for the vindication of creation, and for man's ultimate capacity to understand and enjoy God!"

THE GLORIFICATION OF THE ABSURD

*We evidently retain much of our juvenile attachment
to the mysterious and impossible all of our lives. The
poets, prophets and musicians give rein to fancy, and
let the impossible carry their messages. And the scientists
and philosophers cling to the apparent and the logically
deducible. Probably we cannot ask the poets to become
more practical, nor suggest to the scientists to become
more rhapsodic and oracular!*

I had enjoyed a long talk with Cervantes Saavedra on a pleasant
knoll on which flowers resembling the Grass of Parnassus were
quite profuse. Cervantes said he frequently came to this little hillock
because he admired this beautiful white and green Saxifrage so
much. I was pleased to hear him say this; for back on the Earth it
had been one of my favorites. I found him very well informed in
botany and zoology.

"You are very versatile," I said; "I was under the impression
that you were wholly absorbed in adventure and literature. Your
noble Knight, Don Quixote, is the world's happiest and greatest
burlesque."

"I hoped it would cure my people of their silly knight-errantry
romanticism and medieval superstitions. I was more serious in my
later writings — and not so eager to entertain."

"And you produced masterpieces," I remarked. "However, Don
Quixote not only entertains — it has a purpose beyond amusement,
even yet; and its theme is not presented as an utterly impossible
fiction, from which to turn away with a smile and forgetfulness.
There were, and are, people like Don Quixote and Sancho Panza.
And despite their childlike credulity and hallucinations, they have
unexpected flashes of homely wisdom. Their adventures, interrupted here and there by delightful and heroic novellas, do not

shock us nor annoy us by seeming to want us to believe vague allegories, or revelations of profound mysteries. Your burlesque did not involve the impossible. Its fun, even when nonsensical, was natural and human and very amusing."

"You are kind to express such comments —" he began, when we were interrupted by the coming of a quartet of notables: Schliemann, Goethe, Victor Hugo, and Disraeli. They nodded and saluted, and continued a discussion they had begun, upon the successes of Schliemann and Wilhelm Dorpfeld in excavating the remains of ancient Troy (or Ilium).

As the four strolled leisurely toward the River, Cervantes remarked:

"So, there really was a Troy, and probably a Trojan war, and perhaps a beautiful Helen who caused the war, for the Homer or Homers to glorify in verse!"

"Why," I asked, "have literary minds always been so attracted by the incredible, the miraculous, the impossible and the outre?"

"Perhaps," Cervantes replied with a smile, "with the rest of us, they are weary of hearing so much that is usual, common, forever being repeated over the same pattern. The mind craves variety, contrast, newness; and when the writer achieves novelty the rewards are usually very gratifying. Then, too, one is not hampered by the need to be loyal to established norms and forms, and limited to natural possibilities."

"That is true," I remarked; "how often in reading fiction intended to be realistic, I have said to myself, 'Ah, but that is not what the hero would have felt, or, not what the heroine would have believed, or, not what the mob would have done.'"

"In this connection, I am reminded," said Cervantes, "of a thing I heard Disraeli relating, of which I had never heard. He said that in the ancient Rabbinical lore there is a legend of the Garden of Eden quite different from that found in Genesis. Adam is represented as originally a huge giant. God put him into a deep sleep and removed parts of his flesh, bones and organs, until he was no larger than the average man in historic days. He was given a wife named Lilith. But, for some reason, she was taken out of Eden and Eve was created. The angels became envious of the extreme happiness of these human beings; and a bold seraph named Sammael succeeded in alluring them into disobedience and their fall."

"The version of the myth in Genesis is only a little less offensive,"

45

I replied. "Yet John Milton, a courageous and learned student of philosophy and history, used that childish story as the basis of his most ambitious literary effort. He taxed his faculties to the utmost to produce the most eloquent and compelling language that human percipience could entertain and his genius could create.

"Many earnest and learned men of every generation since his time tacitly accepted the grandiloquence of Milton's prosody as if it were an inspired commentary on holy Scripture. In this they so far abrogated reason as virtually to assent to the implied principle that: Whatever the ancient religious tomes say God has done or commanded, must be right, and cannot be questioned!"

"Yes," responded Cervantes; and after a pause he continued: "I have just wondered whether there was ever a religion which resisted the temptation to attribute human wisdom and the supposed perfectionism of human imagination to the Deity! 'Anthropopathy,' it has been called. The Hebrew religious books begin with it at full blast; and it is continued right into the Christian Scriptures. Only one or two Prophets were gifted with enough insight to even allude to this overt presumption. One of them makes Yahweh say, 'You thought I was quite like you!' As to Milton's theme for his 'magnum opus' — (pointing down to the four characters who had passed us, now standing near the bank of the River) — our celebrated German thinker did the same thing with his 'Faust' and the devil.

"The stories told about Johann (or perhaps George) Faustus were so convincing that some prominent contemporaries actually credited his claim to supernatural powers — among them Johann Gast, Melanchthon and Martin Luther. A man named Johann Spiess published the first version of Faust's career; and it was supposed that the purpose was to present an allegory illustrating the attitude of the religious reformers toward the spreading humanism of that era. It would remind men of the doom awaiting those who rejected the established religious authority, preferring a life of indulgence in natural passions and the alluring culture of ancient paganism.

"Several literary men, including Christopher Marlowe, wrote serious dramas and novels on the Faust theme. The most famous version was the poetic drama by Johann von Goethe. This writer changed the climax of the tale, by having Faust make a compact with Mephistopheles which allowed Faust the privilege to expand his philosophic horizon. In the end he is not damned; but in view of his creditable desire to seek wisdom — and because of the deep devotion he had inspired in Gretchen — he escapes perdition. The implication is, that not a calculating puritanism, but an aggressive intellectual aspiration toward truth, saves the soul."

"Which," I interrupted, "satisfies neither religious school!"

While Cervantes had been speaking another group of Stygians happening to meander in our direction, came nearer and listened. Those I recognized were Samuel Butler, Jane Austen, Charles Reade, Abelard and Heloise, Catherine II of Russia and a group of ladies, Stephen Foster and Eugene Field, a few Australians, and a tall African. Forms and rules of conduct are not as obligatory and uniform among Stygians as they are back on the Earth; and no one was surprised to hear one of the Australians volunteer a few items of no real relevance — until he said one thing in the form of a query:

"Why is it that the literature which the ordinary person sees in Europe, Australia and America, during the past three or four decades, is either so technical and high-brow that only specialists can enjoy it, or, so downright silly, vulgar, stale, flat and unprofitable that a body is ashamed to read it?"

There was a flurry of argument, some condemning, others approving the sentiment. Some English girl suggested that far back in history, a few people in various parts of the world, wrote epics and sagas, chronicles and imaginary narratives — often to celebrate or magnify a federation, a hero, a sovereign and his dynasty, or the national deities. And these writings became the bases of folk tales — often revised, embellished, and altered to suit the times and cultural temperament of the people. She mentioned the Chansons de Geste, the Chansons de Roland — legends of Charlemagne's great paladin — the Arthurian Round-Table legends, the Spanish Cid, the Asiatic Mahabharata and Ramayana, Spenser's Faerie Queene, the German Nibelungenlied, and the English Beowulf.

"How many of these original tales," asked Abelard, "were based upon actual experiences — upon the true records of real events, recorded by reliable witnesses?"

I heard the tall African murmur that probably it was easier to imagine a tale than to find evidence and documentation. No one seemed disposed to begin an argument with Abelard. But Heloise spoke: "Only they with much heart and intelligence," she said, "can successfully write convincing tales from imagination. Writers who must have models for all the nobleness, courage, adventure and sacrifice which readers demand in the dramas they read are too often confined to the usually limited wit and spirit of their models. Truth is said to be more amazing than fiction; but people, as a rule, are poor actors, and cannot maintain a high grade of histrionics on all occasions. But the whimsical Laurence Sterne can excite and hold one's attention and risibilities through a whole chapter written about the wart on an imaginary man's nose!"

It was characteristic of this brilliant woman to be interested in a genius who lived long after her time. Cervantes expressed his approval by a smile and nod to Heloise, and remarked: "I am tempted to believe that most writers have been motivated by the desire to ascertain whether they could equal or perhaps surpass the achievements of early masters. Matthew Arnold's admirable poem on Sohrab and Rustum was taken from the Persian Epic Legend of Ferdausi's 'Shah-Namah' (Book of Kings). And Richard Wagner magnified the barbaric splendor and romantic nonsense of the old German legends of the Nibelungenlied in music which astonished the world. And a recent comer here tells me that — in his opinion — nothing has surpassed the majestic and profoundly beautiful music of his Parsifal. Yet the theme of that opera is one of puerile absurdity in every respect. For that matter, what dignifying of the preposterous can compare with that labored production in unsurpassed poetic imagery and striking metaphors which poured from the vindictive passion of Dante in his 'Divine Comedy'?"

I saw grim dissent in Sam Butler's frown; and on the impulse I jumped into the discussion with a slightly different approach — though I did wholly agree with Cervantes' judgment. I said: "Some of the world's greatest intellects have resorted to the fanciful and the irrational — not to convince others of supernatural possibilities, but to make a point, or teach a lesson, or suggest a new sphere of interest. Ezekiel, wishing to arouse his lethargic countrymen to a determined effort to rise against oppression and battle for the life of their holy nation — told of a vision of his fertile brain, in which the dry bones of those who had been slain in war, arose; and, as he spoke to them, were clothed with flesh; and when he 'prophesied,' the winds of the heavens filled their lungs and they lived! — a great army of the House of Israel! Dean Swift wished to arouse his people to a sense of the inconsistencies and abuses in their political and social life; and to this end, used the wild absurdities of Gulliver and his adventures. Thomas More wrote Utopia to suggest a reformation of ways of living in merry England: a book which was read all over Europe, and had a popularity almost equal to the Bible. Sam Butler, the clever and penetrating critic of his time, wrote a satirical poem, 'Hudibras,' and a romantic Utopian impeachment of modern culture and complacency, called 'Erewhon,' and other fiction — to remind his readers of the folly of cherishing silly tradition, and resisting progress."

(I saw Butler slinking behind Abelard. He retained a certain shyness even on the Styx!)

"And," I continued, "the greatest dramatist that ever graced the Earth, William Shakespeare, did not scorn to use the impossible and supernatural in order to produce his three greatest plays — The Tempest, Macbeth, and Hamlet!"

There was more discussion; but Cervantes and I moved on down to the River, to review calmly a few things we had heard and said. I like Cervantes immensely. He is one of those characters who bring out the best in others with whom they associate.

INCIDENT V

A PAGAN BRIEF

The white-skinned races teach their children to consider themselves very fortunate to have been born into families of superior people. Emerson once wrote: "Every child of the Saxon race is educated to wish to be first. It is our system. And a man comes to measure his greatness by the regrets, envies and hatreds of his competitors." For every one who seeks truth and quality, there are ninety-nine who crave prominence, power, pelf and applause. The growing emphasis upon tinseled sham and bombast and super-colossal immensity, may bog us down to a perpetual childishness!

I was becoming a little weary of listening to long debates on political and national questions, in which the French, English, Americans, and sometimes the Russians and Germans, seemed to take a huge interest; and, to escape a discussion on the United Nations, I had strolled over to a grove of trees resembling the Caribbean almond, where I noticed a number of very primitive people assembled. They were quietly commenting upon the strangeness of the so-called civilized groups which had begun to crowd into the pleasanter parts of the Styx valley.

They were immediately aware of my tolerant attitude and friendly interest, and continued to speak very frankly and critically of the obvious ill effects of "civilized habits," upon those, at least, who had recently left the Earth to join their friends and countrymen for the Stygian interim.

A modest young man who, between the two great world-wide conflicts, had been sent by his tribe to study, and bring back a report upon, the ways and ideas of the rich and powerful nations — and who had succeeded during his travels in getting a university education — was the principal speaker.

His theme was, that the chief difference between the proud and arrogant white races and the humbler people of darker skins dwelling in the wastelands and heather, was simply a matter of education, ambition, wealth and power — and the will and courage to acquire and use them. He held that war was not the rational means of gaining preeminence. He said that he had come to believe that the wise and meek would one day control the Earth.

His arguments were attacked by many seemingly valid objections; but he calmly maintained that the natives of his island had, in small measure, every qualification which characterized the refined and successful optimates of the white skinned nations. He asserted emphatically that he had found the great nations using every social, and civic, and personal, and moral, custom that his own island people had for ages practised. In many cases, he said, his own people had better results than the civilized races obtained.

These assertions provoked many inquiries. Several of the old men asked him to explain how it was possible for the white nations to achieve their wealth and power if, indeed, they used the same customs, laws and personal habits as the inhabitants of wildernesses and desolate islands had always used. "When I left my home," said the youth, "many accused me of the improbity of defying my father. But he is here and will assure you that I had not only his consent, but his very material help and encouragement, to go. I found everywhere, in Asia, in Europe, in America, that family discipline and loyalty were honored and sacred laws. One ancient nation had ten great rules for the moral conduct of its people, individually and collectively; and one of these was the command: 'Honor your father and your mother — that you may live a good and a long life.' This is, indeed, a universally accepted principle. I found everywhere that those societies which evinced a wholesome and admirable dignity and prosperity, were those in which age and age's wisdom were genuinely reverenced. Kinsmen in every nation seem to retain an affection for each other, which prompts them to a mutual concern, even when distant separation makes communication difficult."

Someone remarked that he had been told that evil habits and terrible vices have destroyed more lives than war has — that law was ignored by both the rich and the poor, and that living in the great cities was more uncertain and unhappy than life in a jungle or wilderness infested by wild beasts. "Why then," asked another native, "do these people not have done with such dangers — or depart from their cities and live naturally in the open spaces as we did?" A third speaker remarked: "How can you say that those proud and powerful people have the same laws and customs as our tribe, when we live in peace — each family respecting every other, and defrauding none — while the powerful ones wage war and permit horrible crimes and corruption in high places and low to make life unsafe, and a constant experience of fear?"

I admired the youth's calmness as he replied: "I, too, have been amazed that such shameful incongruity can be tolerated, and that pompous dignity and ostensible refinement can exist in the same latitude and longitude with the lethal toxins of social decay. Indeed, many cannot endure these conditions. The asylums and jails are crowded with victims who have lost all self-control and act as if mad dogs had bitten them; and others destroy themselves, unable to stand real or imagined terrors, or despondent over the loss of ability to enjoy the sense-gratifying or pride-pleasing luxuries and indulgences, or a one-time popularity and influence. Long ago the great rulers of empires, used to keep the poor and the criminal classes amused and half-content by giving colossal entertainments in vast amphitheatres, in which slaves were made to fight each other or savage beasts; and foreign enemies were burned alive, to thrill the low instincts of the ignorant masses. In modern times there are countless devices to amuse and beguile those who want to forget the purposelessness of their existence. Vices of every nature are permitted, as long as they do not obtrude too boldly and embarrass the wealthy people too often.

"Born and reared in such an atmosphere, most people, whether slum dwellers, or aristocrats on clean, quiet avenues, grow so inured to the conflicting elements of law and lawlessness, crime and the 'mild vengeance' of the courts, indecency and perfumed refinement, the rank cacophony of the dens of iniquity and the prideful display of jewels and mink-coats in the opera houses — where the world's greatest geniuses present the world's greatest master-pieces to divert men and women from the wretched and odious realities a few blocks east or south of them: grow — I say — so accustomed to these conditions, that they begin to believe they cannot escape! It is their destiny; why dispute it? To correct the situation is as unthinkable as to give up their present relationships with so many business and social ties! And, besides: as long as it doesn't stalk into their homes by the front door, it is the lesser of two annoyances to put up with it."

A few unimportant questions were asked at this point, which have slipped from my memory; after which, came a part of the discussion which interested me especially, and of which I took many notes. He was asked to name some of the customs which he claimed were universally found to be similar to those of his own tribe. He answered by speaking of the tendency of populations everywhere to divide into two or more groups or parties — some with conservative inclinations, others with progressive ideas. He mentioned a third class — those who had the courage to ignore party lines, in order to help elevate to authority a candidate whose superior judgment and character made him the best choice for the office. He explained that in monarchies and countries under a one-party dictatorship, the democratic functions were reduced to very small areas with limited effect.

He referred to the universal veneration shown to the memory of great men and women, heroes, teachers, poets and artists; also, to the custom in every state to appoint holidays as memorials of significant national events, to keep an honorable history alive in the hearts of the people. He said that all people admire a public-spirited leader, a sincere reformer, and a versatile inventor who can devise methods and machines to make labor easier and more productive; and especially they admire a devoted teacher, who instructs both young and old in better ways to realize the good life.

At this point a woman asked him: "Would you commend the habit of some of our hermits, who spend all their time meditating upon the nature of God, and hunting for inspired knowledge in their own minds?" The youth smiled. "That depends," he said. "Some hermits, now and then, find a valuable truth in their own minds. But, what would happen if everybody became a hermit?"

Another women asked the youth whether all white people were careless about their personal cleanliness. "I was once in a sea-port town for a few hours," she said; "and the men were so unclean; they smelled bad as they passed me — either of tobacco, or rum, or of soiled clothes."

"Most men do reek of tobacco," said the youth; "but in the past three generations cleanliness has become a 'fad.' The makers of soap vie with each other, to produce the most alluring advertisements of their brands of soaps, detergents and cleansing devices.

Many people bathe every day; and most people in 'polite society' are very careful to be as spotless as it is possible to be when they have business or social meetings with others."

This subject led to the matter of personal modesty; and one man wanted to know whether it was true that white people tolerated nakedness in public — and whether there was not considerable variation of standards on this subject.

The young man admitted a variety of standards, but did not think the fact significant. He told them that naked exposure had been more general among the dark complexioned people than among the white — chiefly because the latter have lived in temperate or frigid zones, where complete coverage of the body for comfort became habitual. He said:

"I have been led to believe that the Nudist movement has never amounted to much numerically. Nudists try to exclude adventurers and crack-pots; and only a few dispositions are equal to the resulting exclusiveness from wider association, and the necessity of having an almost religious conviction that Nature intended us to regard every part of the body equally sacred and inviolable. They refer to the idealism of the ancient Semitic story of the Garden of Eden, before disobedience made the primal pair conscious of the impropriety of revealing the condition in which the Creator made them."

"I never thought much of that myth," growled an old fellow. "The first two were married — they wouldn't feel ashamed — and it's certain their Maker wasn't ashamed." I expected amusement in the assembly. There was none. I acquired a new respect for them. The youth added the observation that in his opinion mediaeval and modern art had impressed the white people with the sacredness of beauty in any guise; and that it was conceded that the human form embodies grace, dignity and symmetry to a very high degree. In consequence, clothing and personal adornment are given much latitude, and social custom allows the exposure of face and limbs almost anywhere. Marriage having been mentioned, the youth told the assembly that every race and tribe in the world had marriage-rites, some of them very elaborate and impressive. He added that the laws of every modern nation provide for the protection of the wife, and give her the same legal rights granted to the husband. Hospitality, he asserted, reaches a high degree of refinement among educated and prosperous white people.

"Distinctions of social classes," he said, "are still unpleasantly evident in many places, especially when several races live in the same city. But in all nations there are superior men and women who defy the prejudices of their class, and assume an attitude of equality and genuine friendliness toward those of different racial stock who deserve respect or need help."

"The white people," remarked an aged man, "have for centuries defrauded and enslaved the black people. If they are not doing that now, are they still making weaker people work and remain poor, so that the rich people may grow richer and more powerful?"

The speaker had evidently expected such a question. He replied: "No; other white men with a more sensitive conscience have ended slavery; and wherever economic injustice is revealed, investigation is made, and measures are taken to hold up the offenders to public scorn, and to establish proper relations. Of course, tyrants have, in the past, seized control of governments, and the advocates of justice were temporarily helpless. It is admittedly one of the hardest problems of Parliaments and Congresses to prevent the passage of laws which unjustly favor one class to the detriment of another. The United Nations' authority, approved by nearly every nation in the world, has been created by men who believe it right to give every nation undisputed autonomy, and to every man and woman in every nation, the right to live independently and to pursue the vocation which insures satisfaction and happiness.

"Strangely, the whole world has the same ideas regarding falsity and truth, decency and shame, beauty and grotesqueness, wisdom and folly, loyalty and apostasy, courage and cowardice, justice and injustice, aspiration and complacency, progress and retrogression."

"Why," asked someone, "have the rich and strong nations always made war on each other, and on us weaker people — if everybody recognizes the same good things and bad things you just mentioned?"

"Look into your own heart and mind for the answer," replied the youth. "You, doubtless, have often been angered almost — or quite — beyond endurance, by what you felt was the greed, or cruelty, or stupidity of other people. In your small community your leaders, who were chosen for their good character, adjusted matters, and penalized you, if you used violence or abused the public's patience by over-insistence.

"Nations, even as individuals, are sensitive to the acts and atti-

55

tudes of neighboring nations. In all nations there are groups which feel it a patriotic gesture to publicize their indignation and jealous concern for their own country's honor and sovereignty. Insults invite the same in return. Then, instead of negotiating calmly, before high-mindedness has descended into imbecility — they rush at each other in mortal combat, and destroy a large proportion of innocent, healthy, life-loving youth — among whom are many talented and brilliant sons of sorrowing parents — boys whose genius, had they lived, might have benefitted not only their own country, but the whole world! Finally, sick of carnage and demolition, and in fear of collapse, the warring nations agree to arrange a peace. Strangely, no one seems to ask why this agreement did not take place before the official murder of the promising youth of both nations!"

An elderly native with a quavering voice, added a footnote to this explanation by the youth. "I think," he said, "that the big white nations would not try to destroy each other, if they were as weak and steeped in poverty as our little country has always been. They would have compassion instead of jealous hatred for each other."

A woman then asked whether the number of war-resisters among white races was increasing or diminishing. "I never found any statistics referring to this subject," replied the youth; "but I am inclined to think that there are more determined foes of war today than ever before. While many leading statesmen have attempted to defend war as a sacred duty to escape unendurable tyranny, or destruction by an implacable enemy — and so, to insure national existence — there are, I believe, just as many intelligent people who refuse to bear arms, on conscientious grounds. They do not think it right to try to settle political disputes, or save the nation's 'face' by wholesale slaughter of human beings. The doctrine of 'Reverence for Life' is spreading.

"Every normal person is born with the instinct to learn to discern right from wrong, good from evil. Most people value and develop this inherent faculty; consequently human society is naturally ethical. Before I realized this, I was amazed to find that the intellectual men of ancient Rome — that second 'Babylon,' as it was called — had said many wise and beautiful things, as if enjoying the 'freedom of speech' which was realized twenty centuries later. Cicero excelled in eloquent praise of virtue, honor and truth. Epic-

56

tetus, once a slave, devoted his life to teaching the value of moral conduct and self-control. He is quoted as saying: 'If anyone is unhappy, he is so by his own fault; for God made all men to enjoy felicity and peace.' And again: 'Forgiveness is a sign of a gentle nature; but revenge is the sign of a savage nature.' As if having in mind the terrible evils of war, the famous Emperor Marcus Aurelius wrote in his 'Meditations': 'Men exist for the sake of one another. . . .' 'Reasoning beings were created for one another's sake.' Seneca said almost the same thing: 'Man should be sacred to his fellowmen.' Pliny, the younger, is reported as saying to a friend in one of his letters: 'Never do anything concerning the rectitude of which you are in doubt.' Euripides, a great tragic poet, wrote: 'Silver and gold are not the only coin; virtue also passes current all over the world.' Tacitus, a reputable historian, tells of the high sense of justice shown by the Emperor Tiberius, who absolved a young man from guilt in a revolt, because it was shown that he had acted under the orders of his father."

The youth then spoke of the world-wide feeling of dependence upon a divine help of some sort. Even the most primitive tribes of savages carve deities for themselves out of wood, stone or ivory, and reverence them sincerely. He said: "In every land people erect temples for worship of their deity; and in many religious systems an emphasis is placed upon the seeking for a better, truer understanding of God and His purposes for Mankind. And they believe that reason, faith and study, with an open mind, a determined will and a pure aspiration, will enable them to acquire that understanding, as the soul enlarges its capacity for truth.

"The same virtues and ideals which have moved our little nation to seek a better life, have activated every little and big nation in the world. We had our happy social times on our island — so had, and still have, all the groups of other races and nations. We had our traditions and folk-lore — so have all the old and new dominions everywhere. We enjoyed our experiments in art and music — the white races have carried these to a wonderful perfection! We had our games and sports and contests — you should see the universal enthusiasm over the professional sports, and, the huge Olympic Games, in which the finest athletes of big and little nations contend — with all the world eye-witnessing the events by television, or learning of them by radio reports.

"We were eager to know what mankind had done in the past,

and was still doing. Our parents told us all they knew, and taught us to understand our duties as members of an honorable tribe. Well, every village, town and city on every continent, has its proud and affectionate parents, its schools, and in many cases, a considerable number of graduates from colleges, universities, and institutions for post-graduate research. In short, there is a prominent element in civilization eagerly hunting for truths and facts, trying to discover the ideas which the facts contain, and to separate value from trumpery.

"Our tribe always wanted prosperity with peace, and did not believe in aggressive force with which to snatch such blessings from neighboring tribes. Well, it is a fact, I think, that practically every country under the sun has many — a majority of its people — hoping by honorable methods to achieve these blessings. And these do not consent to intrigue and rapine to procure material gain or diplomatic advantage. They are not deceived by politicians wearing patriotic false-faces! But, alas, as the great American, Lincoln, expressed it: the clever ones 'can fool all of the people some of the time, and some of the people all of the time, but not all of the people all of the time.'

"Those we left on our little island, like the intelligent people of all lands, realize that there is vastly more in the world than meets the eye, or enters the ear. We see that in Nature, and man's contact with Nature, there are inexhaustible fields and phases of being and activity — all of which cooperate to maintain a development of newness and change. Man's curiosity and experimenting have produced amazingly rich harvests, and have given rise to science, philosophy, government and religion, and to related fields of inquiry, such as astronomy, geology, physics, biology, chemistry, mathematics, and other categories of investigation too numerous to mention. Of all the studies of man, that which aims to understand Mankind and its history is most vital and fascinating. The ancient Greeks coined the watchword of wisdom: 'Know Thyself.' It is astonishing how long the human race neglected the analysis of itself. The history of the difficult progress of medicine and surgery is a shocking record of superstitious opposition to scientific investigation of man's physical body! But now he is an open book: his evolution, his long struggle to develop a soul, his bloody, blundering history, with its errors, horrors and heroisms, his adventures and achievements, his slow awaking to true values, his changing opinions, standards and loyalties, his pleasures, hopes and fears, his aspirations and degradations, his nobleness and his bestiality, and his spiritual potentialities!

"Only prosperity, peace and a praiseworthy interest and devotion could have enabled scholars through the centuries to discover and record, for our edification, the vast amount of detailed information found in the great libraries of the world. Our little tribe has had the noble ambition to learn; but it has lacked the practical material means of progress. This lack the white people are eager to remedy. I hope that our clan will welcome their help, with deep gratitude to God!"

At this point the natives who had arisen and were slowly approaching the young man — some smiling, others in tears — surrounded, and then elevated him on their shoulders — singing a national anthem of their own — a very melodious and moving song!

I left the scene, admiring the illustration I had just witnessed, of the way in which the humblest and smallest of human confederations is the whole inhabited Earth in miniature!

UGA IS PUZZLED BY DEFLATED TRIUMPHS

*"Go to the ant, thou sluggard!" advised an ancient
cynic. He went; and learned to be selfish, gormandiz-
ing and savage. Nations of people wage bitter war,
just as the ants do, against others of a different size,
color, faith or way of living. Saints and prophets
warn their people and urge them to avoid hatred and
to seek peace—and are stoned for their pains. Man
will some day rue this acquired obsession of competi-
tive savagery. His weapons will become his Nemesis!*

The intelligent groups on the Styx seem never to tire of discussing
world history. Of course, the nations, young and old, have had no
lack of special pleaders to defend the honor of their governments,
or heroes, whom history has seemed, to them, to have discredited,
or dismissed with slight attention.

A colloquy, which began when Uga, a native of the Canary
Islands in the fifteenth century, asked a small group why every
struggle for improvement recorded in history ended in relative
futility, and, why no social revolution ever completely produced
what it had been its avowed purpose to create — soon attracted
several notables.

Bolingbroke, Chesterfield, Bayle, Defoe and Samuel Johnson
were already there, and others arrived as the discussion progressed.
I approached when I saw that Uga was speaking. I had once had
an interesting talk with him about his unusual tribe life.

"Every society is eminently satisfied with its acquired characteristics," replied Dr. Johnson, "and it automatically resists the innova-
tor, whose proposals always promise to disrupt the even tenor of
established customs, with new methods, standards, and objectives.
And, when the reformer gains enough support to foist his scheme
upon society, the conservatives give it lip-service, and clandestinely,
if not overtly, grasp every opportunity to wreck the development

piecemeal, or totally; or, they content themselves with derisive comment and such antipodal distractions as may hamper or hinder the successful advance of the new ideas."

"After all," added Bayle, "a new idea or purpose ought to be sufficiently fortified by reason and intrinsic probability to overcome the inertia of ordinary conservatism; and, if it cannot remove the natural obstacles which oppose it, it betrays its inadequacy, and ought to fail."

"I had a slightly different opinion," said Uga, "regarding the failure of many attempted reforms. I acquired the suspicion, after much investigation, that almost all revolutions and reformations have attempted too much, and achieved too little. Both the victors and the vanquished are so exhausted when the conflict is ended, that each is willing to compromise. Original promises and hopes are forgotten on both sides. Often, too, the zeal of each has impressed the other, and each side begins to question its own convictions. But in many, rancor, jealousy, vindictiveness have been aroused, and are encouraged by pride. Disinterested observers wonder why the factions did not draw up terms of agreement and co-existence before resort to violence created destruction, misery, inhumanity and hatred — not to mention incompetent statesmanship on both sides! I have asked teachers of every nation and race why Plato's sublime remedy for political chaos has never been attempted in a serious and consummate effort to establish an ideal republic. The reply is always: 'It is too ideal!' "

"What philosophy kept your Canary Island people so happy and contented?" asked Chesterfield.

"There was a minimum of theory, and a maximum of inherent indolence and good-natured agreement to live and help live," replied Uga, and continued: "Laughter was the prevailing expression of contentment with life. It seemed natural to have a feeling of gratitude to the mysterious Source of all good — food, sunshine, health, beautiful fragrant flowers, wholesome social pleasures, absence of enemies, and the happy blessing of home and children. No one ever imagined a happier way to live. 'Improvement' was a strange word to us. Every day the tribes formed large circles, holding hands, and lifting their eyes to the heavens they chanted a thanksgiving for life and all its blessings. We never prayed for better things."

"It is obvious," remarked Bolingbroke, "that your sheltered

existence on the islands explains your bewilderment upon learning how the outside world has floundered in its struggle to find a basis for fraternal relations, and some principle, universally adaptable, by which to establish justice and prosperity. Man's career at large seems to be a perpetual effort to elevate himself to a higher position materially, politically, socially and sometimes, intellectually and spiritually. An instinctive upthrust in his nature drives man to realize the visions he has of nobler or grander spheres of action. He is a natural pioneer, seeking a wider and clearer understanding of a world and universe of mysteries and enigmas — a purer and loftier contact with the esthetic and spiritual realities for which his soul thirsts."

Leonardo da Vinci had joined us, just as Uga started to reply to Chesterfield. He listened attentively to Bolingbroke, and then remarked: "The Canary Islands and Great Britain illustrate a paradox which has had many recurrences. It is the problem of the penalty of progress. The group which is content with conditions ought not be harshly condemned for its proneness to a distaste for change. Any alteration of the existing consuetudes, methods of craft, principles of education or rituals of worship — is likely to be profoundly disturbing. It is interpreted as a threat against the familiar, venerable and quite adequate customs long in vogue and firm in the group's affections. The happier a society is, the less its members feel a need for change. Thus, Nature, if she is really designed to develop the best that human wisdom can produce, appears to have been invalidating such a purpose in every complacent, becalmed, but happy clan or nation that ever wrote its problematic annals for posterity to analyze. On the other hand, when a people is imbued with the ambition to become more percipient, efficient and influential — so many varieties of purpose develop, that often a confusion and discord create a stagnation or conflict, with consequent cancellation of many worthy aspirations.

"We cannot resort to maxims and hackneyed phrases, protesting that 'every good thing is gained at great cost,' and, that 'people value only that which is obtained with much difficulty.' Like so many aphorisms these do not solve the problem at hand; they simply acknowledge the fact, and state the case in abstract. Many whose creature wants are comfortably gratified in a material satiety insist that man is unable to transcend his physiological capabilities — that his reach will always be short of that for which he reaches.

Back on the Earth it was said, 'a man cannot lift himself by his bootstraps.' The assumption was, that Nature intends to teach us to avoid presumptuous and lofty aspirations. In short, we are warned: Don't try to live by hope; don't aspire to hallowed heights; don't attempt to transcend your normal potentialities!"

Several well-known shades had joined the group: Boswell, John and Charles Wesley, Erasmus, Servetus, Pelagius, Bruno, Samuel Clemens, Thomas Jefferson and Joseph Priestley and others. John Wesley spoke: "It is certainly man's prime distinction that he can and does lift himself above the physiological limitations of his nature. Is it not the possession of imagination that has enabled him to transform both his objective world, and his subjective self? Alas, it is indifference to high aspiration that shrinks the soul, and reduces the personality to near non-entity! Tennyson wisely reminds us of the 'mighty hopes that make us men!' "

"Quite right," exclaimed Bruno, "no corporeal sense can perceive the Infinite; truth is not resident in the physical senses — but in the reason, which is the mysterious product of the mind. The eyes of man can see substance, but not the essence of that substance. Most worldlings want to limit human action to the use of corporeal objects — things that satisfy hunger, thirst and other carnal cravings. And they destroy those who reveal an interest in immaterial things and spiritual mysteries."

It was Erasmus who brought the discussion back to Uga's question, namely, how to explain mankind's continual failures really to reform its evil ways, correct its patent errors, and remove the vices and debilitating conditions which too long have defeated the earnest efforts of patriots to establish peace, justice and brotherhood. His first remarks revealed his ever present care to judge justly, and neither praise too highly, nor criticize too adversely.

"Zealous reformers in every age," he began, "have been so eager to abolish the conditions which they judged to be harmful to the social welfare, that they have plunged into campaigns to check and remove tyranny and injustice, and to terminate the lawlessness of the dissipated and delinquent — before they have been adequately prepared. Their enthusiasm eclipsed their normal discretion.

"Consider the great characters who have succeeded to some considerable extent in reaching their goals: Confucius (who once remarked, 'The cautious seldom err'), Buddha, Moses, Zoroaster,

Jesus, Gregory the Great, Mohammed. These men were afire with zeal — but also patient and wise enough to examine every factor related to their undertaking. In one sense every moral, loyal citizen is a reformer; for he is conspicuously active in furthering whatever can be instructive or constructive or of value to his fellow citizens. His example is a positive contribution.

"Reforms have been undertaken since the very dawn of civilization. Modern anthropology reveals how early, primitive tribes formed the habit of trying to find better methods of work, of hunting, of speech, of civic control, of social mutuality, of locomotion on land and water, of skills in simple crafts, of ways to trap animals, of defense against hostile tribes, and of means to learn the will of their gods. The races of mankind are still doing these very things! The same primitive pursuits now have dignified appellatives: technology, industry, semantics, government, sociology, agriculture, transportation, militarism, philosophy, and theology. Modern thinkers perceive more of the meaning and possibilities of social and international developments than did those who lived in my time. But we were awaking to a sense of the truth that mankind's chief objective ought to be the power, in both the individuals and the groups, to achieve self-determination — to be free to seek and to implement discovered truths, for the making of a peaceful and comfortable world.

"The phlegmatic society will not develop conspicuous progress in the struggle for freedom. And the energetic society will usually accept a loose approximation of its enthusiastically preconceived hopes. All the great racial movements were the results of the need or desire to find a better, richer environment. Migrations and invasions and gigantic wars were the desperation measures used to procure prosperity. They produced untold misery, cruelty, disease, and the termination of many promising civilizations. And, while in some cases migrations resulted in advantageous commingling of races, and, in new nations with greater capacity for adventure and creative progress in science, art, philosophy and religion — the great multiplication of ideas, methods, theories, beliefs and purposes which resulted, gave rise to innumerable problems with very few solutions.

"The obstinate barrier to progress toward a desired Utopia, such as my friend Thomas More once dreamed of, has been, of course, man's deep-rooted bellicosity. All the world strives for power to

64

protect wealth, to insure security, and to enjoy an advantageous position. World opinion, however, is increasingly a discouragement to imperialism; and nations now make threats of war only on the pretext of wanting to 'liberate' a people, or to remove a perilous situation created by a hostile neighbor. But wars can no longer benefit any nation, whether aggressor or defender. Even honest minded patriots suffering under the oppression of a selfish conqueror, hesitate to rebel — lest the cure shall be worse than the disease. As the eminent twentieth century dramatist, Shaw, once said: 'Revolutions never lighten the burden of tyranny — they have only shifted the burden to another shoulder.' "

Many notable characters had joined the assembly while Erasmus was speaking. Among them were Thomas More, Dred Scott, H. G. Wells, Santayana, Terence, Seneca, Epictetus, Thucydides the Greek historian, Epaminondas and Pelopidas, Leonidas and Thrasybulus.

Terence addressed Erasmus: "Would you consider that the reforms of Gregory the Great were not a success?" he asked. When Erasmus hesitated, Terence continued: "This singular man, who combined great timidity with amazing boldness, was the son of a rich patrician, Gordianus, a senator. He chose politics as a career; but after serving as Prefect of Rome a short time, he decided to enter the monastic life. When, Pope Pelagius having died, Gregory was elected to succeed him, he did everything he could to avoid accepting. He even requested the Emperor to refuse to confirm his election. After conversing with Gibbon and questioning numerous other scholars, who have given me much material not usually written in histories, I have formed a rather high opinion of this ecclesiastic's genius and capacity, as a manager and reformer. But he is a Sphinx riddle! He was afraid to undertake the papal responsibility, and was constantly the victim of superstitious fears and the thought of his own unworthiness. Yet, he so cleverly interpreted Augustine's teachings as to make them seem actually reasonable and humane. Moreover, he promoted piety by introducing folk-lore elements into the Church's dogmas — especially in the doctrine of Purgatory, which he made popular by assuring the faithful that prayer could obtain the help of departed saints, in the release of souls from Purgatory.

"Notwithstanding his naive ignorance of philosophy and classical thought in general, and his conviction that curiosity was heresy, he was able to unite all factional elements in an unprecedented loyalty to the Church, in an era of darkest pessimism and most barbaric ignorance! And, he comes down in the pages of history as the 'Founder of Medieval Christian Civilization.'

"Well, you have in this first 'Gregory' one who achieved the impossible — and not by political sagacity, diplomatic strategy, nor gory war — but by the potent leverage of his personal character, and an amazing energy, resolution and faith! With all this endowment went a worldly wisdom and keen insight; for, he completely reorganized and personally managed the business matters in which the Roman Church was involved, and used the incomes from many large estates for the relief of the poor. He even negotiated brilliantly with the wild Lombards in northern Italy, and in so doing prolonged the independence of Rome. All of his victories, I repeat, were won — not by military acts or threats, nor by intrigue, concessions and bribes — but by moral authority alone."

"Yet," interjected H. G. Wells, "in a few years nothing of his astounding accomplishments remained. 'The greatest spiritual triumph of the Roman Church' — as it has been called, had faded into the obscurity of posthumous memorabilia."

There were so many comments and variant points of view, which did not shed much light on the subject, that I made no effort to remember them, until Uga once more asked a question.

"How," said he, "ought we to judge the French and American Revolutions, accomplished, as they were, by hate and violence? — And how rate the moral standing of the celebrated leaders and heroes of those times, who never gave a thought — well, a serious thought — to the possibility of obtaining the same, or better, results, by implementing the kind of moral suasion and spiritual power which Gregory the Great successfully used? Would you say that these two victories over monarchical tyrannies had quelled autocratic despotism conclusively? I remind you that the American revolt, in particular, is presented to on-coming generations, as a moral victory. Of course, the ghastly details of battle carnage, the savage fury of men slaying their fellowmen in defiance of the most sacred convictions of the human heart — these horrors — are 'sicklied o'er with the pale cast' of diplomatic discretion! When we view war as the source of demoniacal ferocity, leaving in its wake ruin, bereavement, broken homes and hearts and the wholesale slaughter of promising youth — and with their death the loss also

66

of genius, talent and leadership — how can we call such recrudescence of barbarism a successful achievement? Some timidly suggest that this appraisal ought to be qualified. My friends! You who have been here long enough to feel that your animal nature is effectually transformed, realize that the destruction of any true value is a major iniquity! The sense of value is the regulating influence in human society. The esteem for moral and intellectual values is the factor which molds the character and governs the conduct and attitude of every individual. Hence, our reverence for the life of all who share this existence with us, compels us to consider all historic wars vile abominations. Every consequence of a deliberate purpose must partake of the virtue or vice of its means. In their revolutions and military impositions, men *defeat* higher purposes than they *establish*.

"Asoka, a king in India, after vast devastations in Asia, was overcome by remorse because of the suffering he had caused. He completely reversed the purpose and method of his reign — striving, with every resource at his command, to relieve misery and elevate the welfare of his people and of those whom he had conquered. He lived in the third century B.C. and is still remembered with wondering admiration.

"I think Buddha, Zoroaster, and Confucius scored high in their reforms because they had righteous motives and never forsook them. I am astonished that the absurd Crusades did not teach the Christians of the middle ages the blasphemous folly of wielding the sword of steel instead of the sword of the Spirit! And, I consider that the unexpected permanence of the reforms introduced by Jesus of Nazareth is to be attributed solely to the sublime simplicity of his lofty mission. He taught and lived with two great ideals: Love and Truth. Both find confirmation in the honest and natural heart. Whenever and wherever the groups working in his name fail, or only half succeed, you will find the simplicity of his message has been 'embellished,' misrepresented and marred by theology, ritual, ceremony and impercipience."

Pelagius, the brilliant early fifth century English monk, had been gradually edging his way through the assembly nearer to Uga; and after smiling his approval to Uga, asked permission to speak.

"I have talked," he said, "with that remarkable man Gandhi, from India, a recent comer here, whose ideas and experiences are exceedingly valuable. I urge you to engage him in converse. His

67

work with the suppressed and despised multitudes of India impresses me as a very fair example of a reform which accomplished more than anyone had any reason to expect; for it was an undertaking which bristled with such tremendous difficulties as to discourage any but a spirit of indomitable heroism and determination.

"Gandhi spoke to me of his failures at some length; but he said little of his amazing successes. Of the courage and persistence which he displayed continuously, I had to learn from others — some of them, his one-time opponents. I consider him a wonderful success as a saint and savior. If you are looking for a reform movement capable of converting all or most of the people of a nation to new and better ways of thinking and living — a transformation salutary, disinfecting and reintegrating enough to abolish all social vices, corrupt customs and debilitating superstitions — I fear you will have to wait several millennia, until people become more completely civilized and humanized.

"I am wondering whether future reformers will adopt some of Mahatma Gandhi's methods as he adopted those which he found suggested in the writings of Tolstoi and Thoreau. In any other country, he would probably not have become a commanding figure in politics — at least, not by advocating 'civil disobedience' and non-violent non-cooperation.

"Not many reformers share the hardships of the down-trodden masses whom they try to help. Perhaps Gandhi consciously imitated Jesus. Clearly, he had Jesus' contempt for unjust laws — also his affection for the humble. Gandhi called the 'untouchables' the 'Children of God,' 'Harijans.'

"Like other great souls, Socrates, Jesus, Savonarola, Huss, and countless other martyrs — 'of whom the world was not worthy' — who met death by the violence of ignorant fanatics, Gandhi was slain. His assassin belonged to a rabid Hindu clique which had bitterly opposed any partition of India.

"I, for one, would say that Gandhi's efforts toward true reform amounted to more than those of Gregory the Great. But, no reformation, thus far, has been as effectual as it ought to have been."

There was a silent interval, which signified approval of what had been said. I saw three Greeks with their heads together. Presently one of them, Thrasybulus, spoke:

"The convictions," said he, "of two great friends and leaders of the Greeks, Epaminondas and Pelopidas, confirm my own opinion, that, not only the fall of mighty Rome, but the ruin of classic Greece, and the destruction of other nations and cultures for many centuries, have been due to the baneful yielding to jealous hate and rabid covetousness, instead of a dependence upon intelligence, justice, and a spirit of brotherhood and generosity.

"We sometimes praise the skill of conspicuous conquerors — but we never love them. Yet, men have loved Confucius, Solon, Pitticus, Thales, Socrates, Plato, Buddha, Moses, Jesus, Asoka, and perhaps Hammurabi (whose laws prevented the powerful from oppressing the poor), and Marcus Aurelius (for his moral character and benevolence). They have revered all great workers for human melioration — Rienzi, Bolivar, Savonarola, Luther, George Fox, William Penn, Washington, Lincoln, Gandhi and too-many-to-mention! But who does not despise Sargon II, Cyrus, Darius, Alexander, Attila, Belisarius, Genghis Khan, Tamerlane, Napoleon, Hitler — and the lesser scourges, equally destitute of normal human instincts?"

H. G. Wells spoke at this point. "The effect of the wide-spread social changes in the eighteenth and nineteenth centuries," he said, "both by Marxist influence and by the Jeffersonian theory of equality, were prejudicial to true cultural development. Average people were not able to distinguish genuine erudition from the glib simulation of it. Would-be leaders, depending upon the findings of popular, but out-moded authorities, did not realize that the great problems of science, philosophy and psychology had not been realistically and adequately solved. They were incapable of productive research, and ignorant of any scientific approach to the analysis of facts.

"But these questions were soon forgotten in the great predicament of war — and the following threat of aggressive Communism. The former vexations either solved themselves or seemed unimportant. The two world-conflicts established a new element in the social relationships. All classes suffered greatly, and came out of the conflicts with much higher esteem for each other. The aristocrats feel that they owe a tremendous debt to the 'bourgeoisie,' of whose dependability and courage the wars gave so many proofs. The common men learned how human and likeable the patricians really are. After all — as Seneca said: 'Who is well born? He who is by nature well fitted for virtue!'

"Inherited nobility does not necessarily carry with it the assurance of those salutary traits which distinguish the intellectual, the philosophic, the saintly — or the humanitarian and judicial qualities to which men in the patrician class are traditionally supposed to have some claim. It is often said that standards and ideals as well as customs and manners descend from the aristocratic stratum to the lower strata. History would seem to show that this principle prevails in the decadence of society. That is, it begins its demoralization at the highest level, and the toxic decay seeps through the social grades to the lowest level. So, it appears, that society enjoys its true values by the grace of those at the top, — and also suffers its basest humiliations by the apostasy of the same class. I hoped that an upward trend in bourgeois intelligence and humanity might grow and reinforce the spiritual influences in the West; but, I came here convinced that humanity had run its course; the finale was imminent. What man had sown, he was about to reap."

Santayana injected a remark here: "It should be kept in mind," he said, "that there are other types of citizens to be taken into account when summing up opinions on human problems — and in particular those intellectual groups who have been unselfishly attempting to reduce evils and enrich life by practice of religious principles, and, that solid nucleus of the middle class, whose guiding policy is the 'Golden Rule.' "

Following this, Samuel Clemens, who had been quietly conversing with Joseph Priestley, Voltaire, Martineau and Jane Addams, spoke:

"Fellow Stygians!" he began, "we cannot hope to affect the policies of those unfortunate citizens of the Earth who still cling to life; but to put a blunt finale to this frank exchange of opinions, and to give expression to our pent-up feelings, let me say that there is no historian nor statesman here who has not found in our deliberations, cause to gnash his teeth in mortification that he did not, back on Earth, think of these admirable excuses we have heard, for the abominable failures which we repeatedly made in trying to compel others to do what we so confidently knew would be better for them!

"What we have concluded here, is, that our methods were too slipshod and unstudied, violent and cruel — that meanness means more and meaner meanness: a lesson too difficult for us to learn back there. It is a certain thing — as Uga has said — that our accomplishments always partake of the nature of the feeling and thought we put into them. The quality of our aspirations shows up in the finished product.

"We know now, that we had not the right tools, the right methods, the right blue-prints, nor the rational anticipations, in most of our attempted reforms. The generations which followed us have been laughing at our bungling!

"Let's be glad they laugh at us: It means that they are determined to do better than we did!"

As we dispersed, I said to Havelock Ellis: "Our discussion and its results seem to confirm Uga's contention."

"Yes," he replied, "but it is not always the final decision which gives value to a discussion — it is often the suggested ideas which are met with in the course of the discussion."

INCIDENT VII

WHERE AND WHAT IS HELL?

It seems rather late in the history of this mundane sphere which we inhabit, to find so many sects still speaking and worrying about hell. Evidently the clear insight of the revered Hosea Ballou has not been appreciated by the moderns as it deserves to be. The concept of a merciless, vengeful God is not any improvement over the savage frenzy of ancient human sacrifices to Baal.

I was strolling along the smooth sandy banks of the west shore of the Styx, wondering why it was so scenically satisfying to my human eyes, and suspecting that to the perceptive powers of the spirits stationed there, these environs must be supremely beautiful. This conjecture was confirmed almost as soon as it occurred to me; for, when I rounded a clump of bushes whose heart-shaped leaves glistened silvery on both sides — as I have seen silver-maple leaves shine on the under side — I saw a solemn soul glowering at the charming vista as if displeased with the scene. It was Dante. To provoke him into utterance of his feelings, I said:

"It is a magnificent scene of mysterious and beautiful verdure! I wonder whether every phase of it represents some perfection we missed back on the Earth." Dante's dour and dismal countenance instantly assumed an amiable cast. "It is the flawless quintessence of natural art, supernal and sublime!" he replied.

"Do you suppose," I asked, "that we all see this grandeur of form and color in the same way — I mean, does each one of us see the same or different forms created perhaps by his own concepts of harmonious and symmetrical beauty — or, is the scene before us a substantial, existent phenomenon, whose character and charm some can appreciate and others of us cannot?"

He smiled and replied: "To some extent, we had this problem back on the Earth. Souls are differently receptive, and minds must be trained through the eyes to see the full richness and meaning of the beauty in nature and art. I doubt not we are the same here. You probably see more value and splendor in this scene than I do —for you have lived in a later age in which man's sense of the beautiful has developed to a nobler and deeper appreciation than was possible in my era."

"Not all phases of art," I replied, "have become nobler in modern times! Indeed, many lovers of the beautiful are dismayed that graphic and sculptured arts have degenerated sadly — as if artists had succumbed to a contagion of decline in taste and creativity comparable to a mental relapse into a second and irrational childhood."

Dante's features lapsed into their former severe aspect. "A similar retrogression," he said, "I have observed in other spheres of creative endeavor. Recent comers from even the most respectable nations bring us the most cacophonous succession of sounds which they call 'music!' Sometimes it has a monotonous and primitive rhythm, but never a melody, a meaning, a consistency, nor any vestige of harmony and beauty. It is usually one long repetition of unresolved discords. Yet when I question any of the devotees of this so called 'music,' they insist that they derive as much — or more — satisfaction and up-lift from such tonal tumult and chaos, as from the great classics of Bach, Beethoven, Brahms and Handel!"

A group of middle-aged Americans had stopped near us, and seemed to be interested in Dante's comments upon modern art. One rather handsome woman remarked: "Why do not these modern musicians take their idiotic productions to the savages and infantile groups, where, perhaps, they will be properly appreciated?"

"They think they are educating us to the new and better compositions of tonal beauty," replied a mediaeval musician, whom I remembered hearing on a former visit, singing with Jenny Lind Goldschmidt.

"It belongs in Sheol — if there is such a place!" remarked a serious-visaged Teuton, with a snort.

"Why the 'if'?" asked a sober youth from Texas, U.S.A.

"Because," replied the Teuton, "no one can tell us where it is; and no one can prove that it exists anywhere; and no one can find any trace of the people or person who invented such a place. But

73

once invented, with a devil in charge, there was a plausible explanation — so it was supposed — for all the evil and misery in life, and also a fine excuse for man's selfishness, brutality and all his flagitious debauchery. How could man be expected to resist a spiritual power as potent as this devil who was able to thwart the designs of the Creator, and spoil His beautiful Earth at its very beginning? In this way, reason those who think there is a hell swarming with countless inane demons, and a ruling devil in command!"

This was followed by a lively and confusing outburst of many opinions and convictions — most of them too trivial or illogical to add any light upon the subject. At length, James Boswell spoke. He had come with a group which included Dr. Johnson, Dean Swift, "Lewis Carroll," John Dryden, Tagore, Galeo Gherardi, Francisco della Saga and Tiziano.

"Men were tempted," began Boswell, "to postulate a sinister and nefarious element in the world because they found that their best plans and noblest hopes were the most difficult to bring to successful fruition. It seems like fatuous sophistry to invent an elaborate theological system of ways and means to defeat an imaginary enemy supposed to be able to obtain more influence in man's heart than man's own Creator obtains. But the facts reveal that this invention has deeply and abominably affected the whole philosophy of man's struggle to acquire and preserve an upright character and a pure selfhood worthy of his own reverence.

"Men personified Evil, and made it almost equal to God, because they could not understand that human progress was impossible without the necessary struggling against and overcoming natural obstacles, and the constant exercise of mind and body to obtain and retain strength, knowledge and facility with which to discover and understand the laws of nature, and the appropriate methods to convert the forces of nature into utilitarian means of obtaining food, shelter, security and comfort in human habitations. Every mysterious defeat of man's searching for better conditions tempted him to attribute the frustration to this universal evil power. And evidently the writers of the legends recorded in Genesis were convinced that a constant warfare was in progress between the two great Powers of Good and Evil. A natural human ignorance and pessimism encouraged the spread and perpetuation of this crude superstition.

74

"There have actually been groups of desperate people so fearful of having lost all claims to God's mercy that they instituted a worship of the devil — perhaps hoping to win his good will, and so escape the extreme sting of hell!"

Tiziano had been listening with impatience to speak. Said he:

"Shortly before I came here, in the middle of the sixteenth century, a number of reformers, Anabaptists, Lutherans and others met in Vienna and drew up a set of doctrinal propositions, in order to solidify our organization and proclaim our convictions to the world.

"We were radically different from the Roman Church and the conservative Lutheran groups. I recall that among other things we announced our conviction that Jesus was not God, but man — though a man full of God's Spirit, the son of Joseph and Mary; that there are neither angels nor devils (when a devil is mentioned in the Gospels, the selfish, fleshly element in man is meant); that there is no hell other than the grave; also, that souls which have tried to serve God's purposes, during their earthly life, will be preserved by Him without the aid of any supposed merit said to accrue from Jesus' having been among the many martyrs to the cause of truth and righteousness.

"This meant that, while we held Jesus as history's greatest exponent of pure religion whose truths enlightened and guided us, he did not take the place of God either in our worship or in our private thought. We considered it most probable that the just would awaken, at the end of time, in the Paradise of God, and that the unjust would — like the dumb beasts — dissolve and sink into the dust of the earth, to awaken nevermore.

"We confidently expected our interpretation and hopes to prevail and become the accepted bases of an enlightened and universal religious system. But since coming here, I am greatly perplexed to know what to expect next — seeing that we had no expectation of this delightful interim on the banks of the Styx.

"I should like to add that my comrades and I are astonished that the nations back on the Earth remain so indifferent to the defective and only half-efficient status and scope of their educational and moral systems and religious institutions!"

Upon this there was a hiatus of good natured dispute — especially on the part of some late comers to the group. The confusing exchange of opinions ceased when some tactful speaker began to comment enthusiastically upon the wonders, mysteries, charms and the unexpected possibilities and opportunities, on the Styx, for acquiring new and amazing perceptive powers in every category of knowledge and branch of philosophy. It was Dante who brought the assembly's attention back to the question which insistently asserted itself in the minds of all of us: Who originated the notion of angels and devils, and a hell for retribution upon the unfortunate ones whose psychophysical constitutions by some fortuitous accident incapacitated them for an understanding of — or a compliance with — the laws of natural morality and humanitarian ideals?

"I realize," said Dante, "that when I wrote, my concepts and convictions were too greatly influenced by my passions — my love of what I considered divine justice, and my desire to direct mankind's inclination toward a stricter self-control, a consciousness of the need of purer motivations, a determined resolution to elevate mind and heart, intention and action — until truth, justice, mercy, and righteousness culminate in an exalted and blessed nation! (Dante hesitated here; but no one spoke, and he resumed:)

"In a conversation with that admirable American scholar John Fiske, he suggested that inasmuch as the Author of Nature had conditioned all creatures with the possibility of acquiring, in their racial evolution, the functions and faculties necessary or highly advantageous for a better life — for example, primordial sea-life had to acquire eyes to see both food and enemies — so, mankind has been enabled to evolve protective facilities, among which imagination and sensitive empathy have become prominent. Unfortunately these advantages have been misapplied. Mental perversion, vicious associations, civic rancor and conflict create fictitious images and fears; and these festering concepts destroy the health and sanity of the brain. Neither the foolish nor the wise escape the pitfalls of abnegating nature's purposes and Divinity's intentions. I confess I had no oracular inspiration, no real authority for presenting the figments of my imagination as the actualities of God's hidden eventualities. I will say no more."

"The splendor of your 'Divine Comedy,' " exclaimed an aged Italian woman, "as well as the obvious lessons taught in it, amply justify all you have written!" Dante smiled his thanks, and moved over to converse with her.

At this point a young divinity student, a recent comer, spoke. He began with an apology for entering the discussion, since he was so inexperienced, but pleaded his great interest and concern in extenuation of his boldness. He wished to obtain information which would clarify certain ideas which were in a state of uncomfortable confusion in his mind.

"I have been interested in 'Pneumatology,'" he said, "and that phase of it which speculates upon the existence of opposing groups of incorporeal specters which are said to be mediating between man and God, or, between man and the traditional rulers of darkness and their cohorts. These are they who, Milton says, rebelled against the rule of God, and were cast out of Heaven into hell. 'Nine days they fell!' Though, how, at that period, a day could be measured, Milton would have had trouble to explain!

"Ancient literature reveals," he continued, "that pagan people paid homage to bad as well as to good spirits. Even Plato did not discount the concept; it was universal among average people; and it remained so during the 'dark ages' of European history. Few discredited the belief that frequently the spirits of witches possessed decrepit but innocent old women. It was estimated that at least 300,000 'witches' were executed in Europe during those centuries of ignorance. Intelligent people were rather timid about admitting any disbelief in ghosts, visions, angelic visitations and guidance. Joan of Arc was not alone. And, as late as the 18th century Bishop Berkeley, who died in 1753, wrote of the existence of spirits. And Jacob Boehm of Saxony, Emanuel Swedenborg of Sweden, and Perqualis of France credited the existence of these supernatural beings."

"But!" interrupted a man named Smith from Georgia, U.S.A., "both the Old and New Testaments of the Scriptures treat of these things as true and necessary for our religion. Do you say that people back on the Earth are now repudiating the Scriptures, and that we must all give up our faith in them?"

"No," replied the youth, "I am saying that the reporters of those ancient times did not understand the parables, allegories, imagery, similes, and legends used to inculcate righteous ideals — nor did they distinguish between the true and the false prophets who arose to guide them. They did not realize that the vital truths of religion are very different from superstitious beliefs in supernatural interference in human activities. We are convinced now, that God does not violate His own laws. However, the ethical teachings of Jesus and the great prophets — Hosea, Amos, Micah,

Isaiah — are still the world's noblest and safest guides to man's righteous living.

"Those who, nearly a century after Jesus' death, collected traditions of his short year of ministry, represented him as crediting the belief that demons could possess the minds of susceptible people. And the very pious, to this day, consider it quite wrong to question these reports.

"I found that the authors and the subsequent transcribers of the Scriptures were considerably confused about the nature of the punitive destiny of evil doers, and of the use of terms in stating their surmise. I learned that the words seeming to refer to 'perdition' — such as Sheol, Gehenna, Hades and Tartarus — occur sixty times in the Old Testament; and in the New Testament, Hades is used eleven times, Gehenna twelve, and Tartarus once. In one modern translation in English, First Corinthians 15:35 has been translated, 'O Death, where is thy victory? O Death, where is thy sting?'

"There is no mention of Gehenna in any of Paul's letters — nor is it used in the writings of John, Peter, Jude, the Acts, and the book of 'Revelation.' There is no explicit indication that these names — usually translated 'hell' — were meant to signify a place or condition of perpetual torture — an idea utterly repugnant to any rational concept of a merciful, just and loving Deity!

"Originally, Gehenna was the name given to the Valley of Hinnon, which had been defiled by human sacrifices in the Moloch ceremonies of Ahaz and Manasseh. Later it became a place in which to burn waste and filth; and the dead bodies of criminals were thrown into its flames.

"Most authorities think that Zoroastrianism is responsible for the notion of a powerful and malevolent being who is the villain of all creation and the cause of man's moral imperfection. Zoroaster's remarkable religious system taught responsibility for personal conduct and attitude toward Ahura Mazda (Ormazd, the wise One). Opposed to him was postulated a spirit of darkness, called Angra Mainyu (Ahriman) who constantly afflicted the world with evils. Whether Ahriman was recognized in the system during Zoroaster's life, or introduced later, I have not been able to ascertain.

"It seems that the Jews who lived before the Babylonian captivity knew nothing of any evil spirit named 'Satan,' whose name means 'Adversary.' We do not know who wrote the 'Book of Job'; nor do we know when it was written, though some scholars think it was written during the Exile period by some unknown Israelite. The author uses 'Satan' as the evil character in the drama, which suggests that the Jews had by this time begun to feel the effects of the Zoroastrian superstition."

The young man, suddenly feeling that he had spoken quite long enough, hastily concluded with a feeble witticism: "I think," he said, "that the only benefit conferred by this theological hypothesis of a supernatural dualism is that it has supplied us with a few strong expletives with which to vent our frequent feelings of irritation!"

A middle-aged man from Switzerland, being urged by his companions, now spoke. He said: "We are told very confidently that Jesus accepted the idea of a personal devil. I do not believe it. I consider the references to his remarks upon the devil have been misunderstood, garbled, or falsely attributed to him. To inject references to diabolic powers was felt to be helpful in producing a wholesome dread of them, and a warmer sympathy for angelic powers. This pious habit was prevalent very early, when verbal reports and careless hearsay were passing from lips to ears for fifty or more years — and also much later, when redactors and copyists were making new editions of the Gospels. The common people who were the usual friends and admirers of Jesus, were not scholars and philosophers. The evangelists were still the products of their age; and they had become indoctrinated with the notion of a diabolic force in the world creating general havoc.

"It is impossible to interpret the report of the 'Temptations in the Wilderness' as anything but a parabolic statement of Jesus' contemplations while preparing himself to address his countrymen in an effort to elevate the true values of religion, and if possible avert the threatened dissolution of the Jewish State. Certainly, he never repeated anything resembling the account given by Luke and Matthew. It could very probably be the allegoric fancy of some imaginative follower, to whose personal journals Luke, and later Matthew, had access. Mark simply states that Jesus, weakened by long fasting, suffered disturbing temptations — presumably temptations to imitate the methods of worldly politicians and ambitious adventurers — and Mark wrote his Gospel earlier than Luke and Matthew, evidently knowing nothing of the account given by the other two synoptics.

"I do not believe that the parable of the sowing of good seed on both good and poor soil, told by all three Gospel writers, has come down to us without the presumptuous revision of pious redactors. It has the same flavor of the transcriber's comment and effort to embellish! It is notable that in relating the parable Jesus made no reference to the devil. It is hard to believe that when explaining it later to his disciples he could have said the devil stole the good seed from the immature or shallow-minded. Such a thing would remove all responsibility from those deprived of the seed, and their condemnation would be a colossal injustice — which clearly removes the possibility of Jesus' having taught such a thing."

The factitious flurry of comment following the talk of the Swiss was confused and fruitless. Ultimately, attention was given to a tall handsome man from England, who remarked that the compilers of the earliest Hebrew sacred histories "seemed," he said, "correctly or otherwise to take it as established truth that — whether there is a devil or not — good spirits existed, and were messengers and monitors to earnest seekers of wisdom. Regarding them, primitive myths and legends grew, spread, and developed into articles of faith which became prescriptive and mandatory. The centuries passed; and whatever had 'always been accepted' was considered to be true. To question the verity of beliefs cherished by the forefathers for countless generations would be a rash and rueful repudiation of the hallowed values of venerable antiquity!"

I was glad to see that Charles Reade, the learned English novelist, now entered the discussion. He began by asserting that he had never found any acceptable record of a systematized dogma averring — or any ecclesiastical compendia defending — the existence of angelic beings.

"In my opinion," he said, "the belief in angels was practically universal. It was a pleasant fancy, easily and naturally imbibed in early youth. Supernatural beings and mysterious events and conditions were the favorite themes of conversation — whenever war's rabid insanity abated, and social life could be enjoyed.

"The compilers of the oldest Hebrew tomes evidently had heard some current myths claiming to account for human life on the earth, and trying to explain the failure of man to master properly the problems of his wonderful habitat. They dressed up the mythology as ornately as they could. But they had no adequate concept of the character of the Creator; and they could not make Him act and speak in character. They presumed that the first two human creatures created were led, in some way, into disobedience; and they decided upon the subtle serpent as the villain. The snake succeeded in persuading them to eat forbidden fruit.

"The inventors of the myth did not realize that they were stigmatizing the Creator by attributing to Him cruel and ignoble treatment of His last and noblest creation. For, He was supposed to know all things — and therefore knew that these two inexperienced creatures would naturally succumb to the temptation. Moreover, He also must have known what age-long misery would result. These mythologists even made the Creator assume a deceitful ignorance of what had happened; for He is represented as asking Adam and Eve why they were ashamed of their nakedness! Furthermore, this silly myth was made the authority for woman's subordinate role in life; for, the Creator was represented as condemning her to a complete subservience to the will and whim of her husband. The pitiful consequences of this have been rife through the ages; and are only now being somewhat overcome in civilization.

"However, we must look into more ancient times to find the real origin of the idea of a malign spirit roving the fair Earth, seeking whom he might devour."

Reade ended his remarks abruptly, and no one seemed disposed to comment. I observed the ancient Aristarchus, a versatile genius, born in Samos — a disciple of Straton, who was one of Aristotle's pupils — in conversation with Eratosthenes, the celebrated curator of the library in Alexandria — reputed to be the most learned man of antiquity — whom his admirers honored with the title "Pentathlos." It was he who estimated the circumference of the Earth to be 24,650 miles. (Modern science says, 24,875.) And it was Aristarchus who estimated that the Sun is 19 times as far away from the Earth as the Moon. (Modern mathematics makes it 20 times as far.) These findings, and others of the ancients, were ignored until the time of Copernicus and Galileo, seventeen centuries later.

Eratosthenes now spoke, referring to the classic confusion incident to the problem of finding the origin of the concept of celestial cherubs and infernal imps — and reminding us of the ever abiding difficulty of distinguishing legend from fact, and myth from truth. Said he:

"Epiphanius asserts that the doctrine of two opposing principles was very ancient, and was evidently treated in the books of the Manicheans, all of which have been destroyed. He says that Pythagoras was acquainted with the theory of the two contradictory forces active in the world. Plutarch speaks of the antiquity and universality of belief in an interferential system of good and evil forces, asserting that it is impossible that one cause alone, whether good or bad, should be the sole principle of all things existing; because, God is not the Cause of evil. The harmony of this world seems to be composed of contraries, as Euripides said: 'The good was never separated from the evil . . . that all things may develop the better.'

"We might very properly ask whether the mind of man did not unconsciously anthropomorphize unpleasant conditions into a living force — a personal, autonomous agent, bent upon destruction. For, man was unquestionably aware that some conditions were agreeable, desirable, comfortable, good. He must unavoidably have observed that other conditions were not so good. In every category of human action man finds some things acceptable, others, less so. When conditions and things became acutely distasteful, men called them evil. So 'evil' has become the recognition of the absence of the perfect, the good, or the desirable. Man's sense of values is simply the ability to judge the 'good' by its contrast with the 'bad.' How can he recognize the beautiful, without a sense of ugliness? How can he appreciate light unless he knows the inconvenience and hazards of darkness? In short, is not all progress in social and national life the attempt to improve conditions in every category? And are not wisdom and righteousness good in comparison with the savagery and limited intelligence of the wild beasts?

"Man made a serious mistake in trying to hold some devil responsible for untoward conditions — due almost always to his own sloth and ignorance. Man's further development depends upon his improved sensitiveness to the imperfections in his world, his local environs, his own way of living, and in the quality of his mind and spirit.

"Empedocles, Plato and Aristotle wrote of contrary powers in the universe to which we owe the presence of the beneficent and the maleficent inspirations and allurements which spice our life with variety. Homer taught that almighty Jove had two vessels replete with gifts, one good, the other bad. But Plato criticized Homer for this misrepresentation of the character of God, 'Who does only the good.'"

Victor Hugo, whom I had not observed until he began to speak, now added a short resumé of the argument and comments. In concluding he said: "I am persuaded by the generally brief and vague defense of angels and demons, that most of us consider as highly conjectural the assumption of angelic and demonic agencies, whose aid or hindrance affected our conduct back on the Earth. But I do not think we are suffering any pangs of regret.

"Religion has been too eager to make all people believe *alike* — and generally, to believe the incredible, after the example of Augustine. We cannot find justification for any belief in a retributive hell. The wonders of creation and providence and the mysteries and beauties of the universe speak too loudly of the friendliness and great interest of the whole creation in mankind, its greatest product. And, after all, the glory and dignity of man are based upon his spiritual character, his virtuous aspirations, his independent courage, and his determination to face any eventuality.

"Too much of religious propaganda has been weighed down with insistence upon a belief in supernatural help. All the evidence indicates that the Creator wants man to be brave enough to stand alone, do his best and take the consequences!"

INCIDENT VIII

MATURITY? — WHO IS MATURE?

An artist who can portray great beauty and aston-
ishing likeness—as could Leonardo da Vinci, Michelan-
gelo, Antonio da Correggio, Raphael, Titian, Rodin and
Praxiteles—is gifted with a keen visual and intellectual
perception. The artist's mind and soul have the right ap-
proach to Maturity. His apperception can visualize the
hidden realities under exteriors.

One is always discovering new objects and places of interest on
the Styx — if one is interested in interesting things. On one occasion
I was admiring the perfection of the lotus blossoms resting like
miniature swans on the deep purple lagoon which had eddied into
a small basin on the west shore of the Styx.

A pleasanter astonishment was mine as I looked behind the
arbor vitae which bordered the lagoon! Several superb statues
greeted my gaze. And, working with full engrossment on an
especially noble figure, was the renowned artist Praxiteles! As I
stood looking at the marble in amazed admiration, he, still
oblivious to everything but his work, exclaimed: "Now! but for
that unfortunate slant of the supercilium, it is perfect."

"Nobody," said I, "will know of the slant, unless you tell him."

"But the fact that I know, spoils the image for its purpose," he
replied, still feasting his eyes upon the beauty of his work.

" 'Its purpose'?"

"Yes; it is made to represent 'Maturity.' "

"Just what is wrong with the brow?" I asked, stepping closer.

"It is lifted a trifle above the normal, for such a head — as if the
subject were bored."

"And why is that a defect?"

"The personality which is fully matured is never bored," he
replied.

84

While we were speaking, several notable shades joined us, including Browning, Leonardo, Lincoln and Kipling. No comments of significance were made, until Robert Browning asked why there were so few lines of suffering showing in his face. "Surely," said he, "a mature person feels the sorrow of his fellows, and has endured much himself; and pity carves its lineaments in the expression of the face."

"Nature demands of the mature soul," replied the sculptor, "that it shall maintain such a balance of psychic powers that reason shall erase misery before its marks become indelible. Besides, sorrow is registered in the eyes. Observe; are these not the eyes of Jesus, Spinoza, Debs, Lincoln?"

I glanced at Lincoln, and saw that his facial lines were, after all, not as striking as his eyes. By this time several other prominent characters had joined the group — Julius Caesar, Virgil, Cleopatra, Roger Bacon, Edmund Burke, Zeno (the Stoic), Socrates and several others.

Someone from Mexico asked just what attributes characterize Maturity. At this point I remarked that since Praxiteles had made so great a representation of the Mature Man, he doubtless held some positive and unique ideas on the subject; and, inasmuch as I had never analyzed the mature people I had known, nor synthetically built a mature personality in my imagination, I, for one, would be interested to have Praxiteles tell us what in his opinion this weighty quality of maturity does truly involve.

I was pleased to have Socrates and Lincoln heartily indorse my suggestion. Praxiteles, also, seemed gratified. He responded:

"To determine and express in accurate words the spiritual attributes of a person is more difficult for me than to model them in stone with my hands; but if you will assist me in the proper delineation of these spiritual features, and be frank to object when you think differently, or when my lingual chisel slips, I shall at least give you my ideas, and, in them, material, perhaps, for discussion.

"My statue," he continued, "is neither male nor female, young nor old. It represents Mankind. I have desired to limn a type of person who by complete and reasonable response to every experience, has learned, step by step, what is the wise and appropriate action and attitude at all times."

"Ah," interrupted Alexander Pope, "now we shall learn what constitutes the perfect Man, the regal creature, the crown of creation, clothed in dignity and garlanded with noble beauty! Why has not your statue the victor's crown upon its brow, Praxiteles?"

"The mature person," answered Praxiteles, "continues all through his life to approach perfection. For, maturity is not to be considered synonymous with perfection. The mature person would never consent to pose before the world as a proud victor, much less as a perfect creature — as the laurel crown would imply."

Socrates asked, "Would he parade or even assume that quality called 'dignity' of which Pope and his friends have made so much?"

"I think not, O Socrates. Yet I believe that despite his conscious effort to avoid the simulation of it, some appearance of dignity would unavoidably attach to his whole bearing."

"I am disposed to agree," replied Socrates; "but would a mature man always be so far successful in avoiding an excess of dignity that he would on the one hand never forget how to relax and adapt his thoughts, words and sometimes his actions to the society of the youthful, the very happy, or the very unhappy — and, on the other hand, never let his ambitions, pride or feeling of superiority stamp on his bearing an imprint of austerity or excessive self-evaluation?"

"I think he would be successful to that degree," replied the artist.

"Then proceed, Praxiteles, and forgive my interruption."

"Be good enough to add the stimulation of your wise questions and answers at any time, O Socrates. To return to the question of the scholar from Mexico: 'What are the attributes of maturity,' I am tempted to arrive at them by a process of exclusion, by listing the qualities and traits which have no place in the mature soul. I confess it was by this method I modeled my stone image. The living model was not wholly mature. I had to eliminate certain tell-tale marks which betrayed the presence of immature mental habits, such as self-pity, timidity or fear of being treated unfairly, and a consequent compensatory hunger for fame. Also, the model had an escape-technique of exhibitionism which showed in his eyes and lower lip. He was too fond of sense-gratification — eating rich food and neglecting the cell-creating exercise which a wholesome physical and mental condition requires."

Pericles, the cultured Athenian, spoke here, as Praxiteles paused:

"Would you say, O Praxiteles, that if a man, as well as his parents before him, had avoided excessive emotions and disqualifying social traits and vicious habits, he would develop a symmetry of features and harmony of contour which we would call beauty and nobility of countenance?"

"I am not able to answer that," said the sculptor, "being less a biologist than an artisan with mallet and chisel. But I incline to think nobility would always result and sometimes show in the countenance, and beauty would result quite frequently. At least, my experience seems to indicate this."

Several scientists and biologists in the group assented to this. But, some of the logicians objected to a negative approach. "Let us begin with a definition of the term," said someone. Another voice cried: "No; let us work up to the definition by discovering what the mature person is — what positive traits and attributes of one kind or another he has."

We were about to proceed as this person suggested, when some Englishman from India kept us off the track awhile longer by remarking that variety of cultures, difference of historic times, diversity of theologic and philosophic thought, as well as the simple fact of the universal clash between social classes and individuals, would make agreement impossible; for, said he, the mature man in twelfth century Europe would bear no resemblance to the mature man of twentieth century America. Nor would the mature scholar of ancient Greece have anything in common with the mature politician of modern England.

When it was explained to him that the elements which constitute maturity have to do with mental and spiritual attitudes of Mankind at any time, with no specific reference to local cultures and popular standards of thought, he allowed us to begin; but shook his head, and predicted that we would end in a snarl.

"You will not be disappointed to have me name Serenity as one of the conspicuous elements of maturity," began Praxiteles. "Phidias, Scopas, Myron and I felt strongly that we could and ought to portray the evidences of a quiet, unafraid and benevolent mind, in our sculpture — not only so as to publish to the world the spiritual ideals of Greece, but also to provoke the coming generations of Greeks to emulation.

"It is not the serenity of resignation and patient long suffering, but rather of an inexpugnable faith."

"Faith in what?" interrupted an aristocrat from old Russia.

"Faith in the progressive or benevolent trend of life — faith in the essential good intentions of the Universe — faith in the natural

87

goodness of Man, and, finally, faith in Self. Something of all this is indicated by the popular terms 'poise' and 'repose.' But unless one's conviction is secure enough to be uniform and constant it will not reflect in the external aspect of one's person."

"But," injected Cleopatra at this point, "are there not times when enthusiasm, rapture, emotion, or, grief, pity and desperation preclude serenity? Must one be immature because he or she is normally responsive to the ecstatic or to the appalling things of life?"

"Serenity," answered Praxiteles, "is the name given to a general state of mental attitude. The ecstatic or the appalling occasion is likely to be of relatively short duration; so too the period of response to it must not be long enough permanently to vanquish, or, to immure the serenity of the mind. In one respect your objection is valid. If one should steel his or her mind against all emotional response, it would indicate a motive either of pride, cruelty or idiosyncrasy distinctly juvenile. To be easily moved to tears, therefore, is not a symptom of senile weakness, as some suppose, but rather a sign of sincerity; for age at last teaches the spirit not to dissimulate, not to conceal its true feelings — except in consideration of others' feelings.

"Consideration and gentleness, important elements in serenity, are marks of maturity, and are qualities very difficult to express in stone. I have studied some very rough exteriors — weather-beaten, experience-battered, pain-ridden — in whom, beneath the surface, almost hidden even to an artist's eye, were tokens of good will, sympathy and patience. Serenity is not present when the subject's mind is warped by self-pity or the bias which inclines him to seek and to defend his own reputation, and makes him consider personal gratification and superiority more important than truth and spiritual advancement.

"Gentleness goes beyond the current conception of justice and legal rights. It does not try to judge what might constitute the appropriate discipline for other personalities — unless such a procedure is involved in a charitable service. It assumes that others can and do respond to courteous treatment. Not concerned to augment his own reputation and power, the gentle person is patient under the attacks of others, refusing to avenge himself, and hesitating to humiliate those who oppose him by any defense which might injure them.

88

"In short the mature person scorns the easy method of vengeance and 'getting even.' All this he wisely leaves to time and the natural eventuation of conditions. It is his trust in Man and the Universe, and in the inherent potency of goodness."

"So!" exclaimed a nervous, high pitched voice which I presently recognized as that of Georges Clemenceau, the French politician — "So, it is a token of maturity to trust Man and the Universe! What absurdity! Such an attitude would lead men to disarm and depend upon the will of others for safety and the very means of livelihood. It is independence and confidence in adequate measures of defense, and a knowledge of the vulnerable points of others which gives men poise and repose and dignity. How can a man respect himself when he is indebted to others for his safety and his prosperity? How can a man engage in competition with others unless he is frankly selfish? And how can he command the respect of others if he is supinely tractable, weak and sacrificing?

"Nature put it in a man to flare up in wrath and hot vindictiveness when others try to defeat him. It is his native, pristine manhood asserting itself. 'Revenge' has fallen into undeserved disrepute; but it still retains, in courageous minds, its original character of vindication. A man must safeguard his self-respect — or else who will? He must be 'jealous in honor, sudden and quick in quarrel,' and ready to defend his name against traducement and popular scorn.

"Does not natural history teach this as its first lesson? Observe what honor is given to the lion — because he will not make way for any other beast."

By this time the accumulated disapproval of the group had so surcharged the ether that Clemenceau was, metaphorically speaking, utterly suffocated, and could not proceed. Praxiteles calmly resumed:

"I have not thought it necessary to remind this company that unceasing vigilance and tireless effort and stalwart moral courage must be maintained in a constant opposition to all foes — especially abstract ones — which would destroy first our confidence in spiritual principles and the concrete and objective accomplishments which have fortified our confidence. The mature person tries to make a habit of depending upon the highest possible intelligence — especially when animal passions are likely to bias the judgment.

"It is so difficult sometimes to know whether one is being stirred by 'righteous indignation' or by selfish fury! While the mature person does not weakly seek the middle of the road to avoid conflict or the peril of a hazardous choice, he does avoid the extreme of submission to injustice, on the one hand, and the extreme of puritanic strictness and absolute personal liberty, on the other. He avoids in the same way the extremes of cynicism and of acquiescence and of stoicism and of epicureanism."

As Philip Stanhope mumbled something at this point, Praxiteles addressed him: "Do you wish to dispute this point, dear my Lord Chesterfield?"

"On the contrary, I am happy to corroborate what you affirm," replied the polite Englishman. "However, I qualify my agreement to this extent, that I consider it stimulating and wholesome for the mind to indulge in joyous self-expression at times — especially in youth — when physical energy and a happy prospect conspire to excite ecstatic emotions. But to deliberately cultivate a mood of gaiety, or of solemnity, for the purpose of acquiring either an access to the interests of others or a control of their will, is a contemptible insincerity — of which my associates and I have been too often guilty. The distasteful impertinence of gaiety or of sanctimoniousness is frequently as unsuspected to the perpetrator as it is disagreeably conspicuous to intelligent beholders. I can now see clearly that among social follies this assumption of a mood above or below one's natural manner is one of the most childish. But a prevailing low order of intelligence in men, who hate us if we are more, and despise us if we are less, than they, accounts for, if it does not excuse, this immaturity."

On the Styx there is no need of applause. Chesterfield knew, he felt, the general approval of the group. There was a pause in the discussion; and then Socrates, contrary to his custom, contributed a thought without asking a single question:

"An understanding ear sometimes helps the dullness of the eye," he began. "I find from what has been said that one question which a military fellow asked me awhile ago — as to why the statue had not more self assertion and apparent consciousness of power — is satisfactorily answered. It is apparent now that the face indicates not a compromise between fear and courage, between weakness and strength; rather, a definite, courageous strength which does not spring from, nor depend upon, physical conditions. I am glad, good Praxiteles, that you have made the mature person no potential homicide, no blind, policy-driven patriot, no imperialist."

I saw a heavily built man turn on his heels and walk away — it was Otto von Bismarck. Praxiteles smiled, and, looking toward a group of Americans, saw Mark Twain. "Clemens," he said, "will you seriously or otherwise contradict this assertion of Socrates?"

"Who is rash enough to do that?" he began, and continued: "This is an odd place to learn that War is worldly and silly; but most of the old military fire-belching zealots I have met here have come around to a most effeminate reverence for life, and a most un-martial preference for pacifism. You might almost suspect them of ascribing to Personality a greater value than to Rule, Supremacy and Sway.

"I still think Tom and Huck were justified in their occasional fist fights. The rich and starchy food they ate demanded that they exercise their bodies and stimulate their circulation, or get nasty stomach-aches. But for grown-up people to try to advance an argument or grab a political advantage by wholesale slaughter of their fellow human beings is a vile and fiendish reversion to something primitive, brutish and revolting. I don't like to call it childish. I hate to use the word 'childish' about anything so utterly damnable and insane.

"As to politics, I share the prejudice felt by you fellows down here. There isn't anything sillier than a big man pretending to agree with everybody in order to get everybody's vote. But I would still be a patriot, if I could live again. It would be great fun to demonstrate what a patriot ought to be. Of course, I wouldn't insist my country was the noblest and freest, and could lick every other nation. I'd set up as an arch-critic. I'd write the nasty truth about unjust conditions and the corrupt politicians responsible, the hypocritical big-shots pyramiding their profits on the ignorance and confidence of trustful people, and the trend of so-called democratic statesmen toward regimentation and a repudiation of democratic principles. The new patriot would be a very disagreeable person — about as hateful as Pat Henry was to the genteel Tories of his time, or Gene Debs to the plutocratic stuffed shirts of later days."

"The mature person," resumed Praxiteles, "would avoid becoming an enthusiastic advocate of any sect, school, party or class. He would not be a joiner, a partisan. Do you agree with me, Burke?"

"I was once a strong partisan — for policy sake," replied the eminently fair author of the *Conciliation;* "but it is true that party prejudice has begun to seem very absurd to me. This may be simply my natural reaction to my long and tiresome attitudinizing during my political career. Of course, the principles which call men together and bind them in leagues for the accomplishment of a commonly desirable objective may be quite just and truly applicable at the first. Gradually, however, they undergo variations and amendments, and finally are forgotten. I have asked prominent American and British citizens to tell me the distinguishing political policies of their parties. They could not! Religious bigots are as a rule equally uninformed, unless trained as propagandists, and to this end versed in dogmatics and polemics. Boys love to belong to gangs and clubs; and this satisfaction in feeling oneself a member of a select organization clings long past the time to drop it. Inferior mentalities find a huge satisfaction in sharing the honor of membership in a strong group. It supplies an element of superiority, and confers a dignity, security and importance not to be achieved alone.

"I quite agree with you, good Praxiteles: your mature person must liberalize his sentiments, and must recognize purpose, sincerity and worth in the left wing, right wing, and center — no matter where he finds himself. The mature mind finds that the preservation of integrity demands that it reject and oppose many of the doctrines advanced by the party whose interests that mind has been trained to defend. Consistently mature behavior may wreck a man politically; but it builds an indomitable character."

"It is a blessed good thing for the progress of statecraft that most lovers of their country are not mature!" exclaimed an ancient Greek whom I soon recognized as Lysander the Spartan.

Julius Caesar had been taking notes during the foregoing discussion; and I repaired to him later to learn the details of the debate at this point. Unfortunately, he had been so interested in listening that he neglected to record any of the actual speeches. His notes merely stated that several Americans joined in the protest against Burke's disparagement of political partisanship. Their contention was that without thorough airing of popular opinions the whole truth of political problems cannot be discovered.

Praxiteles agreed, but said this did not demand two or three or several distinct parties, with adherents stubbornly loyal to such policies as struck their fancy, or faithful to such leaders as could make persuasively attractive promises. The mature mind, he thought, would insist upon independent selection of the most honest policies regardless of their source. William James ended the discussion on this point by using his arguments of pragmatic sanctions and forced issues.

I recall one or two sentiments expressed by William James which Caesar did not take down: "When the number of the foolish and corrupt swells to a majority," he said, "it begins to be believed by them that their very size confers validity and authority, that their unanimity proves the probity of their cause, and that their power justifies, indeed, necessitates, compulsion. As for me personally," continued James, "I can respect no authority nor any source of knowledge sufficiently to subscribe — upon its recommendation — to that which, to me, appears fantastic and not founded in the universally accepted canons of reason." At this point a scholar from 19th century China interjected a comment upon Confucius and his ideals. "This great teacher," he said, "was personally most humane and considerate, but he held up as a model, a personality too prone to be self-centered and self-satisfied — a criterion for moderation and good form, but, too proud of negative virtue and useless wisdom."

A new interest brightened the discussion when Praxiteles named Liberalism as a positive quality in the mature mind. A few men, whose careers had been lived in comfortable times and on the crest of incoming tides of prosperity, felt that Conservatism ought to be the appropriate policy and token of wisdom for those who achieve years, experience, and, presumably, maturity. Such arguments as they were able to offer were given scant attention; but everybody was interested to hear the great sculptor's ideas on Liberalism. I can quote a few of his utterances.

"The mature person takes his Liberalism seriously," he said. "He does not, from motives of pride, or perversity, accept a policy called Liberalism, and then subscribe to all the extravagances committed by fervid partisans in the name of that policy. Nor does he consider a course, or idea, to be liberal and acceptable because it is new, or because it is eagerly embraced by considerable numbers of reputable liberals.

"Liberalism does not mean the tolerance of all divergent views or of such doctrines as encourage a hedonistic release from wholesome social restraint. Rather, it is the just appraisal and evaluation of all views. A dullness of esthetic sense is betrayed by over-zeal for opinions, old or new; just as sheer ignorance is displayed by failure to allow for the variety of human tastes and preferences, and the fact that different people actually require different environments.

"A course is liberal when it is the result of a free, fearless and detached study of its causes, its present relationships and its future consequences, with no disproportionate regard to custom, sentiment, private predilection or subsidizing interests. It is necessary for the mature person to give attention to such courses and ideas, since they alone make progress possible. All improvement has spiritual value. And in the ultimate analysis Liberalism is simply confidence in spiritual values. The word itself implies a freedom. It is a freedom conditioned by an integrity which the mature person exemplifies, no matter what excesses and errors may be rife in society under the name of Liberalism."

Someone asked whether Enthusiasm in its popular sense ought to be included as a characteristic of maturity. Praxiteles assented mildly; whereupon Carlyle exploded:

"Unquestionably! It is absolutely essential to the mature character! Come, Praxiteles, you must advocate this trait, and with enthusiasm! For, consider: it is, at times, the token of inspiration or genius; at other times a modest method of publishing deep aspirations, or else it is the determined confession of heroic purposiveness! In many a case it is Man's soul crying to the world: Behold, here is a thing which finds me and conquers me! Give heed to it! In the mature person no enthusiasm would be wholly wrong or non-pertinent; for his other qualities would protect his judgment from such inconsistency."

Voltaire at this point remarked: "Enthusiasm has its small but honored place in the mind of the mature person. But just as men do not constantly feast upon rich and delicate viands nor drink continuously the strongest wines, so they do not manifest their maturity by a perpetual enthusiasm."

The company seemed to feel that this was a reflection upon the prevailing style of Carlyle's utterance. Praxiteles hastily diverted their thoughts by a consideration of the place of Morals in the mature mind. From Caesar's summary I have these quotations:

"In the experienced intellect Morality is inseparably bound to self-respect. But it never becomes a fixed science; for human contacts are too variant, too complex, too unrepeatable. . . . Mature minds must constantly study themselves and surrounding conditions in order to be aware of what is the moral procedure. . . . Morals are 'mores' or 'habits' fixed for awhile by the consensus of opinion of acknowledged sincere people, but subject nevertheless to the bad judgment of provincialism, ignorance, convenience and faulty imagination. . . . The mature person does not condemn as immoral those whose habits are at variance with his, unless they indict themselves as persons of base designs. . . ."

Following this the great artist gave his definition of the mature person: "Maturity is the name of that state and quality of a truth-seeking personality which — considered at any stage of progress — has developed normally in a rational and alert response to total external conditions, and in consistent reaction to normal, interior stimuli. . . .

"I wanted to put a line between the brows of the statue — to indicate dissatisfaction and ambition. But the knitted brow can indicate other sentiments. We know that a full orbed life appreciates the greatness and extent of the as-yet-undiscovered, the increasing conquest of which, the mature mind feels, is imperative. The human limitations which thus far defeat Man's ambitious inquiries into the Whence, Why and Whither of things, do not destroy his curiosity. On the contrary, his slow mastery of his world provokes the very wholesome sentiment of wondering awe. And even if — or when — Man discovers the secret of energy and the nature of mind and matter, he will still want to know the cause and purpose and destiny of these things. And every advance into reality will augment his reverence and wonder and admiration.

"Familiarity with Nature and Reality does not breed contempt: it incites the mind of the mature person to intellectual and spiritual pioneering. Life is enriched for him by the increasing possibilities in quest and experiment, the multiplying vistas of discoveries and emerging truths, the greater definition and clarifying of the data on hand. The soul does not surfeit of knowledge. The mature have taught themselves how to run and not faint in the pursuit of wisdom.

"In every quality the mature person exercises a calm but determined will. I hope the firm mouth and chin of my statue will indicate this clearly. It is this astonishing possession — the individual free will — that distinguishes Man as the greatest animal on the earth. As his soul matures he sees that this will must be used to perfect the relation between the real and the ideal, and to adjust, for productivity, the conditions of his life to the forces in his environment.

"His will-to-live he shares with the brutes, although he glorifies it. The will-to-rule operates in human spheres only — more often to humiliation in the abuse, than to true advantage in the use. Still it is necessary to Man's proper social existence. But it is his will-to-know that lifts him above his antecedents and contemporaries and places him in the sphere of the universal and eternal.

"This will to understand the World and Man's place in it, is the achievement of maturity in mind and spirit. To have it is to possess the power to ascend the mountain peaks, where the light is unclouded and the horizon entire!"

I observed Michelangelo and Scopas in rapid exchange of opinions. There was obviously some serious objection in their minds. Scopas spoke:

"We know, O Praxiteles, that you welcome any fair question, though it imply a criticism. Tell us whether we are right or wrong in asserting that you have succeeded in carving the maturity of *only one* type of personality, in only *one stage* of the subject's development."

"Explain why you think this, Scopas," said he.

Scopas looked at Michelangelo, who replied: "It seems to us, O Master, that *human* maturity cannot be perfectly analogous to the maturity of the vegetable kingdom. A melon, or fig, has many stages of growth before it is ripe throughout, and quickly passes into decay. But a person has many perfections to reach as he passes from infancy to age; and each stage has its ideal beauty. Yet he must repeatedly alter his concepts of truth, goodness and propriety, and his manner of life, in obedience to these developing concepts. Moreover, men reach many kinds of excellence. But, no one person can in his life manifest all types of superior attainment in perception, judgment, and expression.

"We have wondered, therefore, whether it is correct to say that maturity is expressed *in changing action, in mutation of form, and in continual adjustment to the high demands of reason and innate wisdom.* Clearly, no statue in its stationary beauty can represent *change;* yet, a mature soul is constantly advancing toward an eternally approachable ideal. This very advance is an element in his maturity.

"Your magnificent carving here portrays a youth whose wisdom, self-control and integrity are self-evident. But there is no feature nor combination of features which can establish or even suggest the fact that his indomitable purpose is to pursue a perfection of wisdom, self-reverence, and wholeness of spiritual and intellectual coordination. In short, *maturity is too vital, expansive, progressive, and aspiring* — to be chiseled in stone.

"I believe the Supreme and Eternal Artist to be working on the only material which can embody and reveal the soul's maturity as you conceive of it. Once in history appeared a Man who aspired to be, and was, built in the austere pattern of this perfection. And in every age they who would be mature must respond intelligently, feelingly, adequately, to every impingement of the external and internal, immanent and transcendent stimuli of that pattern."

There was silence for a while; then Praxiteles spoke slowly:

"I perceive that I tried the impossible; for, as you say, everything human — even the soul's maturity — is a matter of adjustment to environment and a knowledge of it, which are always changing. The final and perfect human being never *is,* but *is to be.* But my statue does not change; it is static, cold and fixed!"

There was a murmur among the group, which Praxiteles correctly interpreted as indicative of sympathy and good will. Then William Blake, the artistic mystic, spoke: "Not only in art," he said, "but in philosophy and religion and every-day living, we try to reach a goal which cannot be apprehended as fixed in an eternal state. But an ideal is never attained; for it is ever moving on beyond its present status, ever transcending itself, ever stimulating the mind, ever wooing the heart.

"So, maturity is a very real and indispensable goal for every rational being; but, it connotes perfection, and therefore can never be described, nor imagined, nor realized."

Pericles ended the discussion with this appropriate tribute to the great sculptor: "If Praxiteles had produced this image during his life on Earth, he would have immortalized at least one ideal of beauty and intelligence, which might have contributed greatly to human culture, progress and maturity!"

97

INCIDENT IX

WAS JESUS A PHILOSOPHER?

The writers of fiction have explored every method of presenting a striking, admirable, exemplary and ideal character. Biographers have filled countless volumes with the commendable traits and inimitable exploits of their chosen heroes. But who, with the exception, perhaps, of Ernest Renan, has calmly analyzed the heroism and perfection of Jesus of Nazareth, whose excellence is still beyond the imitation and understanding of every one of us?

On one occasion, while exploring an unfamiliar area on the west bank of the Styx, I met a group of mediaeval scholars, a few moderns, and the ancient Empedocles and Democritus. I was fortunate in arriving at the beginning of a colloquy which interested me greatly; one which I had never obtained the opportunity, and right company, to discuss, with any rewarding satisfaction, back on the Earth.

The first words I heard, were uttered by a recent arrival from India. By that very convenient faculty which we acquire upon arriving in the delightful valley of the Styx, I knew the speaker was referring to Jesus of Nazareth. He said: "For one who was not a philosopher, he certainly had an astonishingly consistent and beautiful philosophy of life."

"Who says he was not a philosopher?" I inquired.

"Well, not in the accepted sense of the term," replied the same speaker.

"What," I asked, "makes a philosopher?"

"It seems, my brother," said Empedocles, with a crisp incisiveness in his syllables, which belied the kindly smile on his face, "that a philosopher is one who has accepted or invented an intricate system by which to frame and relate the axioms of human thought-experience. If he succeeds in making axiomatic truths unfathomable, abstruse, enigmatic and impractical, he acquires rank and fame. But if he draws up a consistent system with findings so clear and incontrovertible that intelligent minds feel constrained to govern their thoughts and conduct by them, no one honors him with so dignified a title as 'Philosopher!' If a man says only what you can comprehend, you are as learned as he!"

There was a murmur of dissent; and Empedocles responded by a question. "Which is more important," he asked, "that which determines moral thought and conduct; or that which tries to solve how and why Man thinks and acts as he does?" "Both are important," said a voice which I recognized as that of William James; "but the second is academic, whereas the first relates to realities, values and ultimates. The consideration of these ideas is a forced option for the lover of wisdom."

"I should think," said a Transcendentalist from New England, "that if, as Empedocles and James intimate, the true philosopher is properly concerned with things of the most importance in reality, Jesus ought to have some rank, notwithstanding his apparent indifference to all established systems and all systematized factual data."

"Nonsense!" exclaimed a late nineteenth century Teuton. "He did not write a word; he was a copyist of earlier rabbis; he thought as a sentimental poet — in ecstatic moods and mystic terminology, without logic and reason — he depended upon intuition rather than syllogistic demonstration; and he inherited beliefs which he did not even try to verify."

Someone I did not know spoke at this point in a mild, almost apologetic voice: "Neither did Socrates write, and even the most recent philosophers admit that they are constantly re-stating the ideas and problems of the ancient Greek sages. In my humble opinion the best poets are those who have the most philosophy in them; and Jesus ranks high as a poet. Even in his most mystic moments he never said anything ambiguous or irrational, and the intuitions which well up in a fervid imagination may have a perfectly good and quite irrefutable basis in subconscious mental action. While Jesus inherited many ideas from his God-seeking nation, he was conspicuous for his ability to set aside the inferior elements in his birthright. He was much more successful in this respect than the modern Teutonic philosophers."

"And even if that were not true," observed a smiling Frenchman, who, I soon realized, was Francois Voltaire, "yet would I say that a man must be a philosopher, in both the etymological and the popular sense, in order to be able, first, to design such a career for himself, and, second, to remain consistent with it under every vicissitude and crisis. I submit that it takes a philosopher of some sort to recognize the best moral principles, and that it takes a philosopher to live up to all the implications and involvements of these ethical hypotheses."

"It takes not a philosopher, it takes a fanatic!" exclaimed a thick-necked individual of decided military bearing.

At this point a strange figure caught the attention of the group. He was unknown to me until that telepathic Stygian sense came to the rescue and told me, when I had the requisite degree of concern, who it was: Laócoön, the ancient Trojan priest, who was reported slain by serpents after trying to warn his fellow countrymen against the Wooden Horse of the Greeks. He had several French and German books of Philosophy under his long muscular arm. He spoke:

"Ever since his cruel martyrdom I have been interested in the ideas of this Jesus. A most gentle and courageous character! I have followed the progress of his teachings as they have flown like doves of peace down the ages. Alas, like the dove from Noah's ark — of Hebrew lore — unable to find a resting place! I have felt that whether a philosopher or not he has made all modern philosophy possible — and for several distinct reasons: He saved and made universal the concept of Monotheism; he announced in a voice heard above the clash and roar of military madness, that the soul is invaluable and life is sacred; he established the status of sin as a matter of deliberate selfishness and ill will; and, he placed an emphasis, which time cannot erase, upon purity of motive and sincerity of feeling, with an accompanying scorn of ceremonial and external appearances. Upon this spiritual conception and its unity and ground in a central moral Deity, all progressive philosophy has had to seek its footing."

Then looking at the Teutons he added: "In the face of a popular belief that greatness, security and freedom are obtainable by military success, Jesus said, 'The Truth shall make you free.' And contrary to the bigoted frenzy of his countrymen *who* held it a pious, patriotic duty to hate the Romans, Greeks and Syrians, he taught and practiced a love toward his enemies. And with a world

100

around him gone mad in a desperate search for selfish, individual-
istic gratification, he solemnly insisted that highest happiness results from a generous surrender of one's powers for the benefit of
others.

"But above all," — and at this point he saw Herbert Spencer and
Bolingbroke joining the group — "while he did not consider the
improvement of man and his environment a blind necessity, he did
have a faith in the undefeatable purpose of the Creator, and in the
basic nobility of man.

"He dreamed of a beloved commonwealth in which the rare
souls, the meek, and pure and peace-loving, would enjoy either a
Utopia made actual, or an ideal state of mind and heart in the
very midst of a world full of soulless gorillas, militarists and other
immature types whose feeble spiritual faculties have undergone a
kind of desiccation.

"The adequate socializing of humanity according to the recent
scientists and philosophers, depends upon precisely those elements
which were stressed by Jesus (but which were not comprehended
by his contemporaries, who subjected him to martyrdom): love,
justice, cooperation, reverence for ideals."

As Laocoön paused here, Bolingbroke spoke: "I am as willing
to assent to your asseverations, good Laocoön, as you are eager to
announce them. It has long seemed to me to be an inexplicable
absurdity that the whole world of mankind should be so deter-
minedly divided into those who love and wish to deify this man,
and those who hate and wish to discredit him, *if* there were no
significant and potent philosophy attached to his words and life.

"After all, whose contribution is more vital to the world's welfare: his who speculates upon, and systematizes into epigrams and
syllogisms, the developing theories of being, truth and reality, or,
his whose insight enables him to weed out the adscititious, grasp
the essential, and so live as to persuade and inspire the intellect
and will of all who know him, with virile virtues and spiritual
courage?"

"Philosophy," began Spencer, "is interested in reality."

"Very well," I injected, "and reality is recognized and authen-
ticated by its power to create new conditions. Certainly, no creative
power in human experience is greater than ideal purpose and loyal
character united in high endeavor. This species of reality was
exemplified in the purpose, will and action of Jesus."

"In what sense," asked Bolingbroke, "are we using the term 'Philosophy'? Not etymologically; for we would all admit Jesus to first rank as a lover of wisdom. Not technically; for Jesus had no pet theories developed from established patterns of evolving thought. He seems quite ignorant of Greek speculation; and in so far as Hebrew teachers were philosophic, he was in line with them only in social religion. And we are not using the term superficially, as Touchstone used it when he said to the Shepherd, 'Hast any philosophy in thee?' But if Philosophy is a search for highest truth, in which one bases his findings on incontrovertible experience, and progresses from the known to the surmised and thence to the unknown, then, let Laocoön establish for us his claim that Jesus' methods conform to this definition."

"That," replied Laocoön, "I cannot promise to do. I can only suggest premises upon which you yourselves may reach conclusions. A recent Russian writer named Berdyaev says, 'Philosophy is the doctrine of Man, integral Man.' Now, whether it ought, in definition, to be limited to man or not, it is correct to say, that, in its highest and most significant reaches it is an inquiry into the meaning, purpose, destiny and value of life in its highest form. It is commonly conceded that Jesus has found the highest answers to these inquiries. Does any Freudian here wish to say that such result was the reaction of an over-sensitive emotional nature responding to the stimulus of the libido?"

No one answering, Laocoön continued: "If you wish, we may assume that Jesus was trusting to his animal instincts, voicing his creature optimism, obeying an irrepressible intuition — the heritage of a thousand variant progenitors, many of them mystics. Even so, the same can be said for any genius, sage and superman.

"If, then, Philosophy is the attempt to understand the human world and men's duty in it — Jesus seems to have accepted the world at its worst, and to have proclaimed man able — that is, adequately equipped with spiritual armor — to overcome the evil in the world; in proof whereof he endured all it could give, while still rejoicing in the kingdom of truth and goodness within.

"If Philosophy is, in essence, a search for unity — as Spencer likes to emphasize — then, I ask, is Jesus disqualified because he sought the high union of human societies in a universal brotherhood of peace and good will, the higher union of all men's hearts and spirits in a fraternal bond of love and mutual interest, and the highest of all unities: the affiliation of human souls with the Spiritual Reality of the Universe? Or, doesn't Spencer recognize such unions as philosophic?"

Not giving Spencer time to answer, Laocoön continued: "If Philosophy is the attempt to solve the mystery of existence, the origin and destiny of human consciousness, and the status of man's freedom and responsibility, then Jesus, twenty centuries before Kant and his Categorical Imperatives, took the 'Ought' and 'Must' of duty as established absolutes; and assumed what did not need stating: the unprovable but, to him, indispensable postulates of God, Freedom and Immortality. In a practical simplicity he announced God as Father and Origin of the race; Goodness as man's duty; Truth as the key to Freedom; and Faith as man's comfort and inspiration in an assurance of an appropriate destiny.

"Perhaps some of you call Philosophy the 'Art of Living.' Well, will Havelock Ellis or Ruskin or Santayana offer us a finer example of an artist in this sphere than Jesus? In his total self-expression he exhibited the Stoic ideal of living wisely, and the Epicurean ideal of living happily. Indeed, for the joy of ascending the highest mountain-peak of spiritual ideality he despised what his contemporaries called failure and disgrace.

"But, others of you may say, an indispensable element in Philosophy is an inquiry into the relation between the ideal and the real. So sure was Jesus of the ability of real men and women to stand the gaff, that he made general principles of the theories which in his own life he was constantly demonstrating: Love is the greatest power, so, love your enemies. Resist not evil. Give, and you grow richer in essential values. With God and righteousness as chief *desiderata*, other things fall into insignificance. True happiness is proportional to your unselfishness. Reciprocity is a human instinct; so, bless if you would be blessed. The pure in heart, the meek, the peace-makers are the highest human types.

"Philosophy, you may say, is necessarily interested in Logic, Ethics and Aesthetics. It is apparent from many sayings quoted, however imperfectly, in the Gospels — notably the conclusion to the so-called Sermon on the Mount, the reply to Simon concerning two debtors, the scene of the last judgment, and other sayings — that Jesus was a poet. His illustrations taken from the *genre* and bucolic were evidence of an extreme sensitiveness to the ethical and aesthetic. His thoughts and expressions had the form and substance of logic, even though he knew nothing of formal logic as a method of analysis and synthesis of ideas."

As Laocoön paused here, one of the Teutons murmured, "How could a philosopher make the claims for himself that Jesus made?"

"Those claims," replied Laocoön, "have been misunderstood through the ages, both because his admirers, following the vogue, exaggerated his powers and attributed miracle to what seemed superhuman, and because first century tradition thought it a pious duty to avoid minimizing by magnifying the deeds of its hero. Descartes said: 'I think, ergo, I am.' Jesus, with equal right, said: 'I think, feel and act as a son of a Divine Being, ergo, I am a son of God!' Frankly, I think Jesus' version more important in the history of human culture. You, Empedocles, will agree with me; for there was a time when you felt and declared that your soul was pure and that a god dwelt in your mind.

"Speaking of Descartes, if he was correct in abandoning himself to the good that is in every passion, and in reducing passions into 'nothing more than themselves,' then Jesus was also philosophic and even more in the right in accepting human nature as the proper basis for a divine superstructure, by making the passions serve noble purposes. Thus, sex attraction (condemned in the case of those who sought legal sanction for its abuse, still condemned but forgiven in the case in which no one would cast the first stone, and tacitly approved in the love-blessed rites at Cana), sex attraction, kept pure and restricted, serves the race and lends virility, charm and mystic power to every human quality. Hate, directed — never to persons — but to inanimate conditions which are evil and harmful, leads to reform, to purification, to zeal and determination, to sacrificial devotion. Acquisitiveness, if limited to a longing for the highest gifts, a desire for the enrichment of the spiritual part of oneself; and ambition, another dangerous passion, but not so *if* restricted to a rational self-respect, and expanded to include the welfare of others, these, cease to be liabilities and become the soul's assets. Indeed, the control of these passions constitutes the genius of virtue, and determines the nature of goodness, just as perils determine courage, or labors determine strength. The proper use of these natural passions made Jesus preeminently the touchstone of lofty human nobility, and 'the conscience of the race.' "

Eugene Debs spoke at this point: "In several very gratifying talks with Jesus," he began, "he has expressed many ideas which the Gospel accounts merely suggest. Often I was astonished, as we conversed, to find how inadequate the records of Matthew, Mark and Luke are. Of course, these men were not great-minded enough to understand Jesus; and they often garbled his utterances, or presumed to give to the reader their own interpretation of what Jesus meant. A part of the difficulty, also, was in the translation from Aramaic notes to popular Greek, and again from this Greek — after countless copyings — to modern languages.

"It is not surprising that he was not known as a philosopher. He left no treatises upon the usual themes of the philosophers; and those who cherished his ideals, placed them in a higher category than the vague speculations of the conventional philosophers. The object of the parables was to persuade the troubled heart, not convince the logical mind. His life, however, was the most sufficient and forceful exemplification of his doctrine of fraternity and equality; a teaching which the defective records do not cancel nor injure in the least!"

Laocoön nodded assent and hesitated here as if hunting for another point; upon which William James spoke: "Philosophy, as you have said, is a search not only for truth, but for highest truth; and the human intellect can recognize it only by certain self-evident, pragmatic tests. It is true that Jesus seems to have gone beyond other philosophers in the practical exemplification of the highest truths.

"Whether or not philosophy must ultimately be monopolized by some school of thought," continued James, "Jesus' principle of judging all things by their fruits will place him among the Pragmatists. In one sense, too, he was a Utilitarian; inasmuch as he taught men to seek to provide for all an abundant life, with the greatest good for the greatest number. However, when this came in conflict with goodness and love, he became an Idealist. Yet, in another sense he was a Realist; for he was so devoted to Truth (which to him was fidelity to objective reality) that his idealism did not make him impractical.

"In his pragmatism he went on to purposeful results: the establishment of a happy social order and the purification and spiritualizing of free individuals. Not needing a series of syllogisms on the will-to-believe, Jesus summed it up by saying, 'If a man will carry out in his conduct that which he conceives to be the divine will, he will know whether or not he has interpreted the divine purpose correctly.' And again, he made the Prodigal Son say, when he began to think rationally, 'I will arise and go to my Father.' "

"I quite agree with you, James," said Laocoön, and resumed: "We know from records which could not have been forged that Jesus thought about many practical problems, the solution of which was necessary to moral sanity and whole-orbed intellectual progress. He was the prophet of a civilization in which the individual is able to live up to his ideals without compromise. But, of course, he lived too early in the world's history, and this devotion to integrity cost him his life. For this he is recognized as the great champion of ideals."

"Plato was the true champion of ideals," exclaimed someone.

"That," I added, "is the general impression. But is it correct? What is a champion? An announcer? Put Plato in Jesus' place in the wilderness when he was tempted to use his genius for personal achievement. Confront Plato with the choice between loyalty to the idea that right and truth will win by their own inherent powers, and, the opportunity to give comfort, opulence and glory to his people by the short cut of a diplomatic coup or violent coercion. Ask Plato to select between a compromise with fraud, which brings success and fame, and, a fidelity to righteousness, which involves failure, disgrace and death. Perhaps Socrates could have stood the three temptations in the wilderness, but not Plato."

I repented of the emphasis which I had put upon this not altogether fair contrast; but Bolingbroke courteously covered up my confusion. Said he:

"If the philosopher is true to himself only when he bases hypotheses upon experience or proven factual data or axiomatic truth, then Jesus may be said to be in this sense a truer philosopher than Plato, since Jesus left ideals in their proper category as abstractions of the mind, while Plato postulated certain existential attributes and potentialities to ideals. Pythagoras, Plato and subsequent philosophers did much the same thing in metaphysics as the priests and divines did in mythology: they made as many abstract spiritual existences as they thought they needed for their artificial systems. Plato refined the gross images of the current fables. He supposed a second God, the Logos, the wisdom of the first. Before long, metaphysics peopled heaven and earth as populously as mythology had.

106

"The supposed abstract ideas were wrought up by warm imaginations into eternal essences, incorporeal substances, independent and divine beings, that resided in or with the Supreme Intellect. Bacon properly called this 'the first apotheosis of folly.' "

Several in the group wished to speak; and a general confusion obtained for awhile. Presently the voice of Democritus prevailed. He was speaking of "purpose." Why is the Universe? Why is man? Why is evil? Voltaire closed this phase of the discussion by saying that until modern philosophers can give some rational and satisfactory answer, no one could require Jesus to solve these mysteries.

Some one asked Laocoön what Jesus knew of Epistemology. He replied: "If this be the badge of the tribe, if the philosopher must answer the question: 'How do we know what we think we know?' then Jesus is, at least, an unconscious philosopher, since he feels he knows certain vital truths by the testimony of the inner voice. And I wonder whether the best of the discoveries of your moderns do not come from the same source."

"However," remarked Democritus, "I suppose there is something to be said on the other side."

"Yes," said Laocoön, "Jesus seems to have known nothing about the reasons for existing world-conditions apart from the general idea that God was originally responsible. He was apparently not interested in the nature of mind and consciousness. The systems and theories known to moderns as rationalism, empiricism, mysticism, behaviorism, had no harbingers in ideas expressed or implied by him. He and his contemporaries did not worry about monism, dualism and pluralism. In moral philosophy he could be called a dualist; for he recognized a marked distinction between good and evil, and was represented as accepting the superstition of his day respecting a personified evil. Finally, he did not employ strict logical terminology nor supply scientific data to prove his theories and doctrines. *But,* he was making sense out of experience. Experience has to be grasped and interpreted in language which can be broadly communicated; else it might-as-well not have *been!* Jesus' thought was concerned with self-evident sources, upward developments, and ultimate ideal products. And, I say, he built upon legitimate metaphysics; for, metaphysics is concerned with the fundamental axioms which underlie all common sense, science, and human gregariousness. His great principle of mutuality, the golden rule, subsumes all these categories — common sense, sociology, education, self-knowledge and self-control. For how can you treat others as they ought to be treated, unless you are versed in these things?"

This pleased Democritus; he said: "I find that Jesus said: 'He that *loseth* his life in a good cause findeth his life.' If human experience gives proof that this is so (and I think it does), then Jesus, whether a technician in philosophy or not, has made a most valuable contribution not only to the world's cultural advance, but to the progress of philosophic thought in general, and the support of empirical philosophy in particular."

At this point I spoke again: "Good Laocoön, how would you sum up the argument? What did you seek to establish, and what do you think the ultimate judgment of Jesus' status will be?"

"I wished to show," said he, "that Jesus of Nazareth was most responsible for the best and highest in modern human life, even though he made no conscious use of formal logic; and, that he possessed in his mind and heart the basic elements out of which all philosophy is compounded; and more, he began, in a rudimentary pragmatism and an intuitionalism (not unlike that of the modern Fichte) to lay a foundation in human thought upon which others have built, and which entitles him to a place among the greatest men of all ages.

"Philosophic naturalism is losing support back on the earth because it has too seriously ignored the most important theme of philosophy, namely, human existence. While Jesus felt strongly a personal relationship to the Supreme Mind, his central concern was 'Man.' And, if the discovery of the truth about man will help men to discover the truth about God, then Jesus has established a lead too long neglected.

"If my appraisal of his ideas is halfway correct, it is obvious that modern university education might be enjoying a most powerful factor in the inculcation of a sane philosophy of life by treating the fundamental theses of Jesus — not only as soul therapy — but as essentials for the understanding of human needs, as the bases of moral sanction and cultural stability, and as the metaphysical approach to reality. In short, he reveals in his own life and teaching, that the 'Kingdom of God' is within the possible grasp of every normal person born into the world!"

INCIDENT X

PERICLES PROBES HIS STYGIAN STATUS

It is the opinion of some serious and virtuous thinkers, that Man ought neither expect nor require of God an after-death life of peace and happiness—whether limited or unlimited—seeing what a marvelous privilege it has been to experience the vast variety of wonders in this amazing world. Others, not conscious of being ungrateful, reject this view—especially those who consider they are having a rough and unhappy experience.

Andrea Del Sarto and Cabanel were discussing the development of modern art, while the former painted with meticulous strokes the portrait of a beautiful Jewess whose features he had been studying intently.

When I came upon them, in a secluded glen on the west bank of the Styx, Del Sarto was saying, "If this woman had lived in my day, and I had found her, the world would have had a Madonna compared to which all others would seem pale, primitive and spiritless."

Cabanel smiled tolerantly. "You," he remarked, "could have made this maiden immortal, no doubt."

"I would have made a great Madonna, nothing more. The Virgin is immortal; and this woman is immortal, without my assistance."

"The Virgin is immortal — that is, her name and fame persist imperishably in the memory of mankind," replied Cabanel. "But this girl is not known; unless you tell us who she was and is."

"I did not refer," said Del Sarto, "to a temporal perpetuity of fame, but to the immortality of the soul."

Cabanel looked at the portrait thoughtfully in silence. I approached and found Tintoretto, Borglum, Whistler, Henderson, Ellery Channing and Agassiz gazing in evident amazement, over the top of some low box-thorn at the beautiful portrait. Nearer, lying on the moss, was a group of French students. Presently we were joined by Dante, Beatrice, Cesar Franck, Mendelssohn and some other musicians. I heard one of the students say, "It is fortunate for Beatrice' immortal fame that Dante did not see this damsel first!"

109

"It must be wonderful to be an immortal," said another.

"The master wants personal immortality also," remarked the first student.

"Well, isn't he getting it? — aren't we all beginning it?" asked another.

"Why, no," asserted a third. "This echo of existence down here is merely the twilight of the mental illumination which persists for a brief space, until brooding darkness spreads her jealous wings and expunges every ray, and silent timelessness ensues."

Another student took up the theme. "Very probably," said he, "this flickering animation is not a true existence, before each unit of intelligence experiences the final osmosis and is absorbed in the universal Mind or Being. If Buddha was right in teaching that all beings eternally abide in Nirvana, then that which is taken out of the realm of time loses its contact with substance, is not amenable to the laws of duration and change, and becomes dissolved in the realm of pure Being."

While the student was speaking I saw Pericles of Athens come into the group. He seemed interested in the youth's remarks. "That," said he, "is a rather novel and provocative idea. I have been quite curious about this matter ever since quitting the upper world. It is a great mystery, this sojourn here on the Styx. Every new arrival who has had any valuable thought on the subject — Sabatier, Evans, Edwards, Wm. James, and others — I have eagerly consulted, but am no nearer a solution. Even Lao-tse, Plato, and Spinoza do not commit themselves beyond saying that the Good in the universe is as capable of evolving an adequate spiritual world for the spirits of men as it was of developing a material existence for their bodies and minds."

"Tell us," I urged, "some of the opinions you have discovered, and give us your own judgment of these opinions. We are all eager to discuss the subject."

"I should prefer to listen to someone more capable —" began the illustrious Athenian, when Socrates, who with several others had joined the group, interrupted him: "In your prime you were wont to squeeze beauty and wisdom out of others, as if they were cultural sponges. Now, we shall reverse the process: You shall be the sponge; and though saturated, you shall be squeezed dry by this audience!"

"O Socrates, do you continue even here to audit my soul

and expose me to mine own ignorance? Yet, I suppose I should endure patiently even that pain if it contributes to the pleasure or enlightenment of others."

Several Greeks had joined the assembly, among them Xenophon, who now spoke. "What versions," said he, "of the afterlife have most favorably impressed you, Pericles?"

"That is difficult to answer, since some opinions were impressive because pleasant, others because startling, and still others because logical or rational. But John Fiske's argument, based on the apparent success of nature in answering all the needs and deep desires which she had excited in her creatures, seems to me to have remained in my mind with more tenacity than most ideas on the subject.

"He thinks that one of the basic laws of nature is the constant adaptation of organisms to environment and to the higher potentialities of life. He calls it the consistent corollary to the 'reasonableness of God's work.' It seems to him that since the physical needs and yearnings of lower forms of animal life are satisfied by some provision — often an elaborate provision — of nature, mankind, as the crowning product of life, will not be disappointed in its deepest need and most constant hope. Nature has taught man the will-to-live. He wants to live today. He wants to live tomorrow. He wants to live forever!

"For ages, at first vaguely reaching toward something akin to itself, the soul, struggling for selfhood and rationality, sought for the Eternal, — not in the realm of fleeting phenomena, but in the abiding and eternal presence of Being.

"This is called by Fiske an internal adjustment of ideas achieved in correspondence with an unseen world. Such, he intimates, is the first valid expression of religion in the world; and religion is a factor both too ubiquitous and potent to be ignored when the history and destiny of man are being considered."

"Are not those grapes too green to be crushed into palatable wine?" asked Aesop. "I no longer ridicule the failures of men; but I still feel that most human experience is frustration."

"Well, the hypothesis does lack what the moderns might call pragmatic sanction," replied Pericles. "However, a recent moralist in America, John Holmes, insists that the greatest advances in science have been made by the learned investigators who went as far as they could with mathematical proofs and then jumped in faith to an inferential conclusion. It was thus that several important chemical elements and mysterious, unseen substances were discovered. It was thus that Neptune was found before any human eye had seen it. Indeed, it is the common rule of life to act upon the highest inference in faith.

"Often a set of equations and symbols will lead to a perfect theoretical answer; yet — the logicians tell me — they simply do not fit the facts. For ages men depended upon Euclid's geometric propositions as necessary, basic laws in the science of measurement. But now, men use not three, but four, five, six dimensions to find symbols to represent cosmic relationships. The biologists and chemists report similar changes in their theorizing.

"Holmes insists that these arguments of logic, faith and inference are identically the proofs used by modern science — which no one questions — and are equally incontrovertible."

"There is one significant difference," remarked Roger Bacon; "it is this, that in physical science the result of bold symbolization can be, and mark well, *always is* corroborated by actual experiment before it is accepted; whereas in the mystic realm of cosmic spirit there has been no tangible confirmation, no factual, resultant Q. E. D."

There was quite a storm of protest upon this, many insisting that the evidence lay in the reality of power of mental ideas, and in the secondary effects of spiritual impulse on material conditions. Someone remarked: "Love cannot be weighed and measured with mechanical gages but its effects are unmistakable. Observe what it did to Abelard, Petrarch, and the Brownings."

Pericles, gaining attention once more, remarked that he quite agreed that "in terms of temporal and material entities, abstract realities, conditions and forces — among which human passions may be numbered — do produce indisputable changes, some of which are permanent. But," he added, "is any one of you prepared to assert that the abstract desire of a portion of the human race will of necessity coerce the universe into the enacting of a virtual miracle? I use the future, 'will coerce', because it has not yet been demonstrated, and hence is a hypothesis for the future to verify."

"Why," asked Alcibiades, "do you call it a miracle? Is not mind shown by William P. Montague and others to be a substantial essence? — and is not matter indestructible? Montague says that the chances against the fortuitous arrangement of the atoms of the living body into cells, chains of cells, reflex arcs and systems of such arcs, would be a quadrillion to one; that obviously the whole organism is regulated by a Gestalt, or *active form,* or field. He says the life or *soul* can be considered a form of potential energy, in correlation with — but independent of — the atoms of the body; and, that as such it is not subject to dissolution and extinction."

"Montague's admirable thesis deserves serious consideration," replied Pericles. "Whatever exists must have a form, whether humanly tangible and visible or not. We know that all existences are in a state of flux. As long as they are changing they remain temporal, that is, they exhibit duration. Perhaps temporal change will never cease. The heavy earth which we have recently left may disintegrate into invisible electrons, yet its electronic constituents would remain temporal entities.

"We are asked to contemplate 'a potential energy' with sufficient materiality to be amenable to the laws of temporal mutation, and yet sufficiently ethereal, spiritual or incorporeal to escape decay and structural dissipation. How anything that depends upon temporally controlled forces in a world which evolved and sustained it, can exist when, or if, time-space duration ceases — is a problem not soluble by human intelligence. It must, therefore, require what is called a miracle.

"We seem to have in the *mind*, as Montague says, a force with the characteristics of substantiality, — a hierarchy of matchless complexity and delicacy, directing the detailed activities and long-range purposes of thought and desire, — a governing principle must have quantitative reality; for if this *mind* were a volatile effluence from brain cells, an electric emanation or energy, and only that, we would have an unexampled instance of the product producing itself. However, the question remains: Can this *mind* operate anywhere, that is, outside of its brain and nerve cells? Is memory registered anywhere else? Do hope, desire and aspiration ground themselves in our self-consciousness by any other roots than the sensory nerves of our physical bodies?"

Some humble woman from India asked a pertinent question: "There was a time when on the earth there was neither brain-cell nor mind," she said. "If nature or God joined the one to the other and made intelligent human beings, why can he not repeat the transmutation in another, glorified life?"

"I can neither confirm nor refute the implications of your query," said Pericles. "You evidently suppose that there is a realm yet to be experienced by us in which, all cosmic clocks having stopped, and the celestial orbs no longer revolving to measure duration, all entities once conditioned to material laws,

113

will become — let us say — electronically transmuted, or miraculously converted by divine fiat, into a more glorious compound whose characteristic is changelessness. And Montague evidently supposes it possible that *life* or soul or the *potential* energy of the individual can exist in a non-spatial, non-temporal void, in mystic association with other souls and that greater Life by the sufferance of whom it has had its brief earthly sojourn.

"Well, there is no precedent, no analogy, nor any universal human expectation available to lend probability to that."

"With God all things are possible," exclaimed an American evangelist.

"But not all things are desirable," added John Burroughs.

"But," I ventured, "there may be some divine design which will make it a highly desirable thing to perpetuate individual personalities. Besides, we are not going to declare immortality impossible simply because we cannot offer incontrovertible theories for, and indisputable evidence of, it, are we? — or *are* we?"

Much to my astonishment Charles Darwin answered. "That would not be wise," said he. "Life originated in inorganic matter; and no one can even imagine the underived or radical source of kinetic energy and chemical affinity. Possibly from the chrysalides of mind-electrons there will issue immortal souls — why not? But where they will go and what they will do *ad infinitum*, I have not the wit to image!"

Pericles appeared puzzled for a moment, then resumed: "While the arguments from analogy and from the evidence of matter's indestructibility and the continuum of duration do not seem conclusive, yet it may properly be asked, as Darwin's comment suggests, whether it is, after all, a kindness to man to ask him to endure forever. Eternity is really a long stretch. I image that after the equivalent of nine hundred and ninety-nine nonillions of centuries one would begin to grow tired even of variety itself.

"I have talked to men who, back on the earth, were ambitious — and still are — to know all their intellects can retain. Leonardo told me he expected to make thousands of mechanical tests and learn all the laws that govern the action of things on the earth and in the stars. Just how his experiments are to be made if matter is to be changed into a spiritual something, I do not know. Hildebrand told me he was going to learn every detail, even the smallest, of the history of the Church, when he gets settled in heaven. But where he will get his books, manuscripts and other sources, he did not reveal. Havelock Ellis remarked that he was happy to anticipate having leisure at last to properly investigate many mysteries in the cultural evolution of primitive man. But must not the data for such research be at least material enough to be seen, touched and heard? Are we to surmise that remote conditions and primitive ideas are also to be perpetuated by a spiritual metastasis?

"Herschel, a perfect gormand for knowledge, was rejoicing in the expectation of visiting Antares, Sirius and Mira, as well as Mars, Saturn, Uranus and Jupiter, to learn the truth regarding these great bodies. I replied to him, 'That will be wonderful, — provided they still exist.' Some enthusiastic scholar said to me that he had no fear of becoming weary of eternal life; for in an infinitude of space there must be correspondingly unlimited opportunities and variety. I could not agree with him that there *must be*. I cannot imagine one corner of creation snuffed out of time-space, and the remaining parts preserved as a paradise in which disembodied spirits may eternally disport themselves.

"A young Scotchman told me he impatiently awaited the happy occasion when he should be able to embrace again his beloved family. I spared his feelings by not referring to the inevitable and immeasurable confusion which would accompany the reuniting of all the links of 'loved ones' in the genealogical chains of children, parents, grandparents, great-grandparents — back through the branches of the family trees whose entanglements grow to vast proportions as you recede! I fancy too, that many a person would be glad to escape the necessity of associating again with some of his relatives."

"The Christian system," remarked Mohammed Aben Alamar, "is very unsatisfactory in its doctrines regarding the hereafter. The description of paradise was hazily sketched by the unimaginative authors of the New Testament; and later writers, even the scholarly Bernard of Cluny, timidly remained within the pale of ecclesiastical authority. But in trying to improve upon it, my own religion made it absurd."

"The Greek conception of Elysian fields was much more varied and interesting, but no less irrational," said Pericles, and continued: "I am inclined to think the argument based on the goodness of God presumptuous. It assumes that we know what is ultimately best for us; and it dares to suggest that God ought to take cognizance of this and act accordingly. It says in effect: 'It is an injustice and a ruthless frustration of universal human aspiration to deny man immortal life.'

115

"In my youth, when I was weary of unsatisfactory activities and social follies, I often drank wine until I was sleepy, then sank into welcome, dreamless oblivion, to forget the shallow nonsense of my world and be unconscious of my own inadequacy for awhile. I still think it was no hardship to be out of life in that fashion. Injustice is a painful condition; but in lethal sleep and perpetual oblivion how can one suffer anything, even frustration of aspiration? The thought of extinction is truly repugnant to a person in the prime of his physical and mental health. But it becomes less and less intolerable as he comes to a maturity of reason and self appraisal.

"If one's life has been a series of triumphs, or a pleasant, gently flowing stream through fragrant meadows and peaceful valleys, must one then fear to die lest a contrary kind of experience awaits him? If one's life has been hard, bitter, painful and disappointing, will one then demand a compensatory career? In any case, is the posthumous adjustment to be on a jurisprudential or a business basis — so much peace and ecstasy to compensate for so much misery? — or so much deprivation and pain to balance the superfluous pleasures or excess privileges of the former life? How can we attribute such judicial travesty to the governing powers of the universe!"

At this point William Bryan, an American politician, spoke: "Religion in all ages has exercised a wholesome check upon the selfish and cruel instincts of undisciplined men and this fear of retributive justice and a righteous punishment for sin, has been an indispensable power both in the state and in society, to keep law, order and decency from being flagrantly and continuously violated. It is a foundation principle in all religions — especially the Christian."

"The sense of justice," replied Pericles, "is so strong in men's minds that when they violate it, they become alarmed. They have lost integrity and self-reverence. They cannot face themselves and their fellowmen — much less God. Imagination, tradition and established authorities create a great variety of dogmas and convictions on this subject; but a calm consideration of nature's ways, particularly of that department of nature resident in the spirit of man, will make it appear at least presumable that eternity is not needed for compensation or for punishment.

"Human experience reveals that man protests against having his soul audited. He knows he pays for his indiscretions, and tries to avoid them from motives of practical expediency. His

116

reason refuses to reconcile the ascription of perfect justice to deity and the vile dogma that this deity is eternally hateful, and vindictive, and punitive beyond all proportion to the guilt. It amounts to a blasphemous imputation against the rationality and benignant purposes of the creative Mind.

"Even the Christian Church does not carry to their logical conclusions the doctrines it has been afraid to discard concerning the fury of a supposed angry God, and the incomparable bliss of those elected to salvation. If the death of a saint were celebrated by anthems of joy and a holiday for happy thanksgiving, we would say the church members were acting consistently with their belief in the after-life of unalloyed felicity. But, the mourning, the lamentations and solemn requiem for even the saintliest, indicate too plainly that religious optimism has not dissolved the mystery of death."

Upon this, Roger Williams, who had been admiring the beautiful Madonna Del Sarto was painting, turned and remarked: "The Heavenly Father desires his children to think of things true, honorable, beautiful, inspiring! Moreover, the universal horror in contemplation of the eternal damnation of moral rebels and religious heretics would be insupportable; the firmer the faith in the infernal tortures, the greater the collapse of civilization, culture, intelligence and sanity, under the pall of hideous fear and an irresistible hatred of God."

"But," asked Pericles, "do normally intelligent men really expect the deity to sit in posthumous judgment against them? Sin is generally considered to be a symptom of disease, either mental or physical or both. Merits for supererogatory beneficence are no longer seriously esteemed as bonds paying interest in Elysium. Abnormal psychology, whether leading to altruism or misanthropy, calls for present therapeutics rather than future requital."

Pericles paused while a group of Americans from the southern states withdrew. Eugene Debs broke the silence. "The zealous pressing on for the glories of divine prizes," said he, "is distinctly immoral insofar as it is an ignoring of present duties, a scorning of true glories here and now, a selfish obsession to acquire the undeserved, and an impugning of divine impartiality. The indirect effect of the popular belief that mankind will find atoning delights in an after-life has been to harden the hearts of materialists and capitalists. The abuses of the mine, factory, cotton fields and department stores are the results. Industrial slavery, now prevailing all over the world, is the logical outcome of rejecting the intellectual freedom which spiritual truths offer men. It is conceivable that such a religious superstition might persuade a whole nation of people to feel justified in the hideous business of military conquest against an alien people having a heathen or unorthodox religion — as a check upon the generating of countless souls doomed to an eternal perdition."

"Not only conceivable, but actual, my dear Debs!" replied Pericles. "If, on the other hand, men could become fully aware of the unescapable limitations of earthly life, and realize that to none is 'another chance' granted, it is certain they would appraise life with a new appreciation, and try to make the brief, mysterious passage of consciousness through time as significant and pleasant as possible for themselves and their fellowmen."

"The fear of punishment and hope of reward," interrupted Horace Bushnell, "are certainly not proper and ethical reasons for upright conduct. 'Human morals as Santayana says draw their vigor from earthly economy, and find their sanction there'. But, I am thinking of the great hosts of unhappy victims of disaster, disease, and the cruelty of others. Is the universe, without an afterlife, altogether fair to these poor souls?"

"Our immediate craving for happiness," answered Pericles, "is so monopolizing, that, like a blinding blaze before our eyes, it blots out all other finer, nobler and more appropriate lights. Experience as such, may be all nature cares to give us — hoping, so to speak, that in it we will find a combination of internal and external conditions favorable to our making a positive contribution to the world's life. Men are not intelligent enough to measure and balance happiness and sorrow so as to give the soul a full-orbed experience. The most miserable life may be capable of developing a capacity for a mystic, secret ecstasy. Perhaps sorrow itself enriches and ripens and perfects the soul and gives it new and thrilling sensations or profound satisfactions, — that the bones which Jove has broken may rejoice.

"I remember that in a cluster of grapes the sweetest ones were smallest. In a forest, I fancy, the trees dwarfed and smothered by the giant trees are not without some compensation. Whatever the explanation, nature is not anxious about the individual; and that fact should make men — in whom nature becomes ethical — genuinely solicitous to bless and comfort their fellowmen."

"Then you would make the individual's obedience to his instinctive urge to be compassionate the measure of his saintliness," remarked Bushnell.

118

"I would at least name it as a very pertinent reason why a sacrificial consideration of others is consistent with the most dignified human aspiration," replied Pericles.

Edwin Booth quoted Hamlet, ending with ". . . perchance to dream; ah! there's the rub!"

"I have often wondered," said Cabanel, "whether the mind might carry on some sort of ethereal, non-substantial existence, with the power to remember, and, as Hamlet said, dream — perchance dream some very ugly stuff, too, if the mundane career of the mind had been defiant of conscience and common charity."

To this Pericles replied: "If dreaming is more than memory — and it seems to be much more — it would involve many corpuscular elements of the mind whose survival is called in question. In contrast to all this some metaphysicians would establish an identity between the *absolute,* the *perfect* and the *eternal.* They say that to immerse the thought and emotions in these absolutes and truths is to be absorbed by the *eternal.* To live in the ideal so as to impress its image on society is to live on in the lives of others. They say that apperception of the perfect is the mental appropriation of immortality; that sincere sympathy with divine graces is a virtual participation in the ideal or eternally divine; and that this rational eternity is the true spiritual and imperishable glory of makind."

Tagore, the venerable Indian scholar, remarked at this point: "Yes, O Pericles; many poets have insisted that the appreciation of reality and the entering of the psyche into the sublimities, truths and universals of life are the valid and only experiences of eternal verities. The island universe of stars a million light-years from the earth, and all this connotes about past and future eons, is the popular analogy of infinity and endlessness. But the pivotal, climacteric point is the *here and now.* All essential, permanent value crowds into the present. God himself can never be more necessary and immanent than in the present moment. Now is always the accepted time."

"That mysterious essence called 'life'," began Pericles, "may, indeed, be utterly independent of time, duration, space, and so-called eternity —"

"But certainly!" exclaimed Aesop with evident amusement. "Man lives in an imaginary present. The past follows his footsteps like a shadow, so closely that no haste can avail to shake it off. The future as irrevocably resists his approach. And between the past and the future no blade is sharp enough to enter. The two

119

come together with the weight of two eternities in perpetual, inseparable contact. Only the imagination can place a separation between them. Yet it is in this imaginary, non-existent *present* that man lives. How attenuated, beyond mental comprehension, must *life* be to find its rich and varied experience in a locale so timeless, spaceless and non-existent as the *present!"*

Pericles smiled. "Almost you persuade me, Aesop, to doubt that I was ever alive," said he. "But I am reminded to consider that if I *never was,* I would have more reason to accuse nature of unfairness than I have, as the case stands."

"Spirit," said someone, "evidently permeates the universe. Can we not believe that human spirits are fragments of the universal Spirit?"

"— As chlorophyl is bottled sunshine," injected a Canadian student.

"Possibly," resumed Pericles. "And, if these spirits or life essences of men do indeed have God as their destination as well as their origin, and, like the rivers of the earth ever flowing toward the great purifying seas, they flow into God, for whom they have so evident an affinity, — then, the character of eternal life will be determined less by the nature of the temporal tributaries of small, weak human spirits, than by the vast benevolence and purpose of the divine ocean, the absolute Life, the eternal God."

Pericles hesitated; and Socrates, who seemed to be waiting for something more, addressed him: "Come, Pericles, do not stop; let us have your conclusion."

"Well, O Socrates, it seems to me that this strange essence called 'life' is truly an entity too mysterious for our chemistry, our philosophy, and our imagination to analyze or comprehend. There are other such mysteries. Possibly, the universe has been going through a vast cycle in which life, once a unity in God, was radiated through the cosmos, finding its way to congenial hosts and habitats, and its highest form in the minds of men; and, that this life will flow back again to its source, as rain drops falling upon the place beneath perform their mission and find their way back to the ocean. Then since divinity is not static, a new flux of active creativity — such as the original explosion of space-force, which resulted in our island universe — may launch a new and perhaps a more spiritually refined creation.

"If it is not too, too hypothetical, O Socrates, I would suggest that with each succeeding cosmic evolution the basic elements of creation must become vastly more potential and versatile, and saturated with beauty, sublimity and God!"